STUDY GUIDES

to accompany
The United States in Literature

SCOTT, FORESMAN

Scott, Foresman and Company
Editorial Offices: Glenview, Illinois

Regional Offices: Sunnyvale, California • Tucker, Georgia • Glenview, Illinois • Oakland, New Jersey • Dallas, Texas

Preface

These **Study Guides** are intended to help you provide for the abilities of all students. Step-by-step questions are to be answered on the *Study Guide* page as a student reads a selection independently. For students in the lower half of your class, the *Study Guides* will be useful in bringing them to the point where they can discuss a selection in class. With many selections, however, you will want to assign *Study Guides* to the whole class. This work is not intended to be graded, but you may want to check from time to time to see that students are using them profitably.

ISBN: 0-673-27139-0

Printed in the United States of America.

12345678910—MAL—9897969594939291908988

Unit 1 The New Land

Unit 2 Literary Nationalism

Unit 3 American Classic

Unit 4 Variations and Departures

Unit 5 The Modern Temper

Unit 6 Modern Drama

Unit 7 New Frontiers

Unit 8 The Red Badge of Courage

Unit 8 Three Long Stories

Name Class Date

A Spectacle of Great Beauty

by Christopher Columbus

Beginning the Selection

Read the title and the biography on page 8. Then read the first part of the selection, up to page 10, where Columbus writes, ". . . they valued it as highly as the most precious jewel in the world. . . ."

1. In his first two paragraphs, Columbus describes some "islands." What name did Columbus use for the islands? What are some of them now called?

2. Below are four things Columbus mentions in his letter. Next to each item, list some of the words Columbus uses to describe the item.

   trees:

   birds:

   season:

   clothing:

3. Columbus tells his men not to give the people of the islands "worthless articles." What are these "worthless articles"?

4. How did the island people treat such articles when they received them?

Continuing the Selection

Finish reading the selection, answering the questions as you read.

5. Columbus writes that the island people believe that he had come from "that place." Where do the islanders think Columbus comes from?

6. What do the island people call Columbus and his men?

7. What plan does Columbus think King Ferdinand has for the island people? Why does Columbus think that plan might work?

Thinking About the Selection

8. Columbus draws a clear portrait of the people he found on the islands. Summarize his impression of them.

Name Class Date

Read the notes on pages 12 and 13 before reading the following American Indian poems.

The War God's Horse Song

Navajo

1. Who is singing this song?

2. In the first part of this song, the narrator describes his horse by telling us what it is *like*. There are two lists below: a list of nouns referring to parts of a horse, and another of nouns describing what that part resembles. Draw lines matching each part with the appropriate description.

hoof	stars
fetlock	round corn
legs	striped agate
body	eagle-feathered arrow
tail	lightning
eyes	eagle plume
ears	black cloud

3. In describing his horse as having a mane made of rainbows and stars for eyes, what do you think the narrator is saying about his horse?

4. Think about the line "I am wealthy from my horse." What does it mean to you?

5. The last line of the poem is "I stand for my horse." What meaning of the word *stand* do you think the narrator has in mind? Why?

A Dancing Song

Pima

1. What does the title tell you about the kind of song this is?

2. Read stanza 1. How is the singer feeling? What might be making him or her feel this way?

3. What does the singer find in the bog water?

Name Class Date

4. What is the subject of the second stanza?

5. In the third stanza, what does the phrase "I run in rattling darkness" mean?

6. The last line in the song, "running to that singing place," seems to take the reader back to another part of the song. Where?

Firefly Song

Ojibwa

1. In this song, the narrator uses three words to describe the firefly. List them in the sequence they appear.

2. What is the narrator asking the firefly for in the first two stanzas?

3. In the third stanza, what does "white light sailing, white light winking" refer to?

4. A "refrain" is a regularly repeated phrase occurring at the end of a stanza. What is the refrain in this song?

Three Fragments

Quechuan, Dakota, Ojibwa

1. In the Quechuan fragment, what are the shadows the water bug is drawing toward him?

2. What kind of dream do you think the singer is describing in the Dakota fragment?

3. Name one thing the Quechuan and Ojibwa fragments have in common.

4. Pick any one of the fragments and write a line to follow the last line in that fragment.

Name Class Date

from **The Iroquois Constitution**

Dekanawidah

Read the biography of Dekanawidah on page 18. Then read the excerpt from the Iroquois Constitution all the way through.

1. In the first line of this selection, Dekanawidah refers to the Five Nations' "confederate lords." Are these lords on Dekanawidah's side? How do you know?

2. In the opening paragraph, Dekanawidah refers to a person or a group of people as "you." Who are the people he addresses?

3. The first paragraph of the Iroquois Constitution focuses on a central image. What is that image?

4. After Dekanawidah and the confederate lords uproot "the tallest pine tree," they do three things. List them in order.

5. An "emblem" is an object that symbolizes another object or an idea. In the second paragraph, Atotarho is crowned with a "sacred emblem of antlers." What does this emblem signify?

6. What qualities will the wearer of the antlers have?

7. In the third paragraph, Dekanawidah gives directions to the lords to give thanks before opening each council. Circle the items in the list below that are *not* on Dekanawidah's list of creatures and spirits to thank.

animals	lesser winds	guns
maize	fruits	lakes
beads	tools	herbs
streams	moon	great winds

8. *Dwell* means to "live." Where does the Great Spirit live, according to Dekanawidah?

Name ______ Class ______ Date ______

from **The Narrative of His Journey**

Alvar Núñez Cabeza de Vaca

Beginning the Selection

Read the title and the biography on page 23. Then read the beginning of the selection to page 24, column 1, where each man regrets his fate and "that of his comrades about him."

1. The biography tells the story of how Cabeza de Vaca's family got its name. Invent a family name of your own choosing, then write a brief history of how that name came about.

______

2. What do the Indians get from Cabeza de Vaca and his men in return for the food they bring?

______

3. Describe the events when Cabeza de Vaca and his men try to leave the island.

______

Continuing the Selection

Read the rest of the selection, answering the questions below.

4. What did the Indians do when they discovered the Europeans' plight? Why do you think the Indians responded in this manner?

______

5. Cabeza de Vaca feared that if he went with the Indians, he and his men would be sacrificed. What actually happened to them?

______

6. The people of Malhado had different ideas about curing the sick than the Europeans. How did the two kinds of medicine differ?

______

Thinking About the Selection

7. On a separate piece of paper, write an account of the visit to Malhado by Cabaza de Vaca and his crew as though you were one of the islanders.

Name Class Date

Making Peace with the Illinois Indians

Robert de La Salle

Beginning the Selection

Read the biography on page 27. Then read the beginning of the selection to the end of the paragraph on page 30, column 1, where some of the Indians take "three days in returning from their hiding places."

1. In the first two paragraphs of this narrative, a clear picture is drawn of an Illinois Indian village. What do you learn about the village and the way of life of the Illinois?

2. La Salle decides to take the Indian corn. What does he plan to do?

3. One of the Illinois chiefs on the other side of the river watches the confusion his tribe falls into when La Salle and his men arrive. Why do you think he stops his men from shooting?

4. The French negotiate with the Illinois before they speak. What do they negotiate? How do they do it?

Continuing the Selection

Read the rest of the selection and answer the following questions as you read.

5. After the feast, La Salle calls the Illinois chiefs together and tells them that there is a "matter he wishes to explain." What is it?

6. What information does La Salle want the Indians to give him about the river?

Thinking About the Selection

7. Imagine what would have happened if one of the warriors had discovered Illinois corn in the French canoes before La Salle was able to tell them he had taken it. Write a short paragraph describing the events.

Name Class Date

The New Land

by John Smith

Beginning the Selection

Read the title and the biography on page 33. Then read the beginning of the selection to the end of the paragraph on page 35, column 1, which begins "Thus, though all men be not fishers . . . ."

1. In the first line, Smith asks what could make a person happier than to "tread and plant ground" he has purchased. How has the ground Smith is talking about been purchased?

______

2. In the first paragraph, Smith asks a series of questions. Who do you think he is addressing these questions to?

______

______

3. The four questions below have been paraphrased from the first paragraph. Number them in the order in which they appear in the selection.

_____ What is better for a person's honor than to discover the unknown, build towns, populate countries, teach the ignorant, reform what is unjust, and find work for the idle?

_____ What could make a person happier, especially someone with little money or only his abilities, than to plant ground he has acquired by taking risks?

_____ If he has any faith, what could he do that would please God and humanity more than to convert the Indians to Christianity?

_____ What could be more pleasant than building a future from the untouched earth, with God's blessing and his own hard work?

4. At the beginning of the second paragraph, Smith says, "Here nature and liberty afford us . . . ." Where does he mean by "here"?

______

Continuing the Selection

Read the rest of the selection and answer the question below.

5. Smith writes "My purpose is not to persuade children from their parents; men from their wives . . .", etc. Who, then, is he trying to persuade?

______

______

Thinking About the Selection

6. Put yourself in the place of one of Smith's original readers. Would his account have convinced you to come to America? Why or why not?

______

______

______

Name Class Date

from The History of Plymouth Plantation
by William Bradford

Beginning the Selection

Read the biography on page 38, and the title and subtitle on page 39. Then read the beginning of the selection to the sentence on page 40, "And the next day they got into the Cape Harbor where they rid in safety . . . ."

1. What information can you discover about this selection simply from reading the title and subtitle?

2. What story does Bradford tell that demonstrates, in his opinion, God's providence?

3. What problem occurred that made the passengers afraid the ship might not complete the voyage?

4. How was this problem solved?

5. A disaster befalls one of the passengers during a big storm. Who is the passenger, what is the disaster, and how is it resolved?

6. In each of the first four paragraphs, Bradford mentions God. Make a list of these references. What do they tell you about his view of God?

7. The Pilgrims finally sight land. What is the name of the place they come to? What do they do there?

Name Class Date

Continuing the Selection

Finish reading the selection, answering the questions below.

8. Once they arrive in the harbor, the Pilgrims fall on their knees and thank God that they are in "their proper element." What is Bradford referring to?

9. The Pilgrims find themselves in a desolate wilderness. What familiar comforts do they miss?

10. What kind of welcome does Bradford report receiving from the Indians?

11. Below is a list of the nouns Bradford uses to describe Cape Cod. Fill in the blanks with the adjectives Bradford uses to modify these nouns.

storms: ______

coast: ______

wilderness: ______

barbarians: ______

beasts: ______

winter: ______

12. What added fears do the Pilgrims have about the master of the ship and crew?

13. Bradford mentions "the brethren at Leyden." Who are they, and what are their feelings toward the Pilgrims?

14. Why can't the Pilgrims turn to them for help?

15. What does the prayer at the end of the selection tell about the Pilgrims' view of their voyage?

Thinking About the Selection

16. Imagine that you have come with the Pilgrims to Cape Cod. Write a short paragraph describing what you see and feel that first night.

Name Class Date

Traveling in the New Land

by Sarah Kemble Knight

Beginning the Selection

Read the Comment on page 43 and the title and the biography on page 44. Then read the beginning of the selection to page 45, column 1, where Knight writes, "I began to think on the transactions of the past day."

1. Knight introduces two very different characters in the first few paragraphs of this selection: John, her guide, and Debb, the daughter of the family with which Knight will be lodging. Make a list comparing and contrasting their characters, as seen through the narrator's eyes.

John: **Debb:**

2. Describe the "parlour" where Knight spends the night. What words does the narrator use to color your impressions of her lodging?

Continuing the Selection

Read just until you come to the poem that Knight addresses to the moon.

3. Knight describes the meal she receives at the next stage of her journey. Do you think she enjoyed it? Support your answer.

4. What personal qualities come through when Knight writes about crossing the river in the canoe?

5. Looking ahead to the next river crossing, Knight imagines what will happen to her. What are her worst fears?

Name Class Date

6. What do you think Knight means when she compares herself to a "Holy Sister just come out of a Spiritual Bath"?

7. Once it gets dark, Knight's imagination takes over. What does she see in the forest as they travel through it?

8. How does Knight manage the second river crossing when they finally come to it?

9. The journey does not grow easier for Knight. Describe some of the things that she worries about after the river crossing.

10. What happens to revive Knight's spirits?

Continue reading until the end of the selection, answering the questions.

11. To whom does Knight dedicate her poem?

12. Which part of her journey is the poem about?

13. What does Knight mean by "thy Bright Aspect"?

14. Knight's journey ends on an agreeable note. How does she envision the forest?

Thinking About the Selection

15. Think of a difficult journey you have made. What similarities can you find between your journey and Knight's? What differences?

Name Class Date

Bears

by William Byrd II

Beginning the Selection

Read the title and the biography on page 49. Then read the beginning of the selection to the end of the third paragraph.

1. According to the biography, what was William Byrd II doing when this account begins?

2. What does Byrd say "proper culture" will do for the grapes he finds? What do you think the term "proper culture" means?

3. What was the bear Byrd's party killed eating?

4. Byrd gives three reasons why bear meat is preferable to other meats. What are they?

5. What is it about bears that made Byrd and a few others initially "squeamish" about eating them? What information does he give as a reason not to find eating bear an unpleasant experience?

Continuing the Selection

Read the rest of the selection, answering the questions as you go.

6. Byrd describes bears as a "clean feeders." What does he mean by this?

7. *Provident* means "to show thought about the future." In what way do bears lack this quality?

Thinking About the Selection

8. Byrd shows the methods by which bears get two different foods. Pick one of the bear's methods and describe it in your own words, using the same kinds of details Byrd uses. What behavior does the bear exhibit?

Name Class Date

The Trial of Martha Carrier

by Cotton Mather

Beginning the Selection

Read the title and the biography on page 52. Then read the beginning of the selection to the end of the third section (III).

1. Look up the word *indict* if you don't know its meaning. What is Martha Carrier indicted for? What is her response?

2. Mather writes, "Martha Carrier, or her shape," tormented her accusers. What do you think Mather means by "or her shape"?

3. What happened to the bewitched people at Carrier's trial when she looked at them? What happened to them when she looked away?

4. What did Carrier's children confess to? Why wasn't their testimony used?

5. Do you believe the confessions of Martha Carrier's children? Why or why not?

6. What does Benjamin Abbot claim Martha Carrier did to him? When did Abbot start to get better?

Name Class Date

Continuing the Selection

Read the selection through to the end. Answer the questions as you read.

7. What were the names of the people who accused Carrier of bewitching their cattle?

8. In what way were the testimonies of Foster and the two boys similar?

9. In his conclusion, Mather calls Martha Carrier a "rampant hag." Look up the words if you don't know the meanings. What is Mather saying about her?

10. What kind of person do you think Martha Carrier was? Use information reported in the selection to draw a portrait of the accused.

Thinking About the Selection

11. Most of the people accused of witchcraft were women, and most of the people who admit to being witches in this particular account are women. What conclusions do you draw based on this information?

12. Put yourself in Martha Carrier's place. Write your defense of the charges made against you by one of your accusers. Use the first-person point of view.

Name Class Date

from **Sinners in the Hands of an Angry God**
by Jonathan Edwards

Beginning the Selection

Read the title and the biography on page 58, then answer the question below.

1. What does the title tell you about the selection? What kind of sermon do you think you are going to read? Why?

Continuing the Selection

Now read the beginning of the selection to the end of the third paragraph, which begins "Thus are all you that never passed under a great change of heart . . . ."

2. *Wrath* means anger. To what does Edwards compare the "wrath of God" in his first two sentences?

3. What does Edwards say will happen when God takes his hand from the floodgate?

4. How does Edwards perceive God in this first paragraph?

5. Who is Edwards addressing in this selection?

6. How do you think Edwards feels about the people he is addressing?

7. In his second paragraph, Edwards uses another metaphor for God's anger. What is it?

8. Who or what bends the arrow and strains the bow?

9. What keeps the arrow from being released?

10. In the third paragraph, Edwards refers to "a great change of heart." What do you think he means by that?

11. What does Edwards's sermon suggest as one way to avoid God's wrath?

Name Class Date

Read the rest of the selection, answering the questions below.

12. Edwards thinks that some people won't believe what he says about God. What happened to others who didn't think they would suffer?

13. Edwards uses yet another metaphor to describe God's view of the sinner. What is it?

14. According to Edwards, what is the one thing that saved his listeners from going to hell during the last night?

15. Edwards tells his listeners that they could have gone to hell at any time. What three specific times does he mention?

16. Describe the danger that each sinner is in, according to Edwards.

Summarizing the Selection

17. Use the space below to list the main ideas in Edwards's sermon.

Thinking About the Selection

18. Having read and seriously thought about Jonathan Edwards's sermon, do you think you could present another perspective on God? Write a letter to Edwards describing your view.

Name Class Date

To My Dear and Loving Husband and **Upon the Burning of Our House**

by Anne Bradstreet

To My Dear and Loving Husband

Read the biography of Anne Bradstreet on page 62. Then read the entire poem, answering the questions below.

1. Who is this poem addressed to? What do you think the author feels about that person?

2. In the first line, the poet writes, "If ever two were one, then surely we." What does she mean?

3. Bradstreet values her husband's love more than what valuable items?

4. What image does Bradstreet use to evoke the strength of her love for her husband?

5. Do you think Bradstreet's husband loves her? Why or why not?

6. What does Bradstreet propose to her husband as a way of living forever?

Upon the Burning of Our House

Read the entire poem carefully, then answer the questions.

1. In the first stanza, what is it that Bradstreet does *not* look for when she goes to bed?

2. In stanza 1, Bradstreet refers to things heard to evoke the fearfulness of fire. List all of the words that relate to sound in this stanza.

3. In stanza 2, who does Bradstreet turn to for strength?

Name Class Date

4. What attitude toward God do you think the third stanza reflects?

5. What does *repine* mean? What does Bradstreet mean when she says "Far be it that I should repine"?

6. In stanza 4, what has God done that Bradstreet takes as an example of his justness?

7. In stanzas 4 through 6, Bradstreet names the things she misses and will miss. List five things that she "sorrows" for.

8. What do you think she might be doing in these three stanzas?

9. At the end of stanza 6, Bradstreet writes, "all's vanity." What conclusion has Bradstreet come to about the loss of her possessions?

10. For what does Bradstreet chide herself?

11. What metaphor for God does Bradstreet use in the eighth stanza?

12. Though her house has burned, Bradstreet claims she still has a house. What kind of house is it? Where is it?

13. Where does Bradstreet conclude that her wealth lies?

Thinking About the Selection

14. Think about the last time you became angry or unhappy about losing something. Using Anne Bradstreet's philosophy, describe on a separate sheet of paper how you should have reacted.

Name Class Date

Huswifery

by Edward Taylor

Read the biography on page 66, the Reader's Note on page 68, and the poem's title, then answer the question below.

1. The title of the poem, "Huswifery," refers to the spinning and weaving that housewives traditionally performed in Taylor's time. Why do you think Taylor might have chosen this particular title?

Now read the entire poem, answering the questions.

2. What metaphor does Taylor use in the poem's first stanza?

3. Below are some of the words that appear in the first two stanzas of the poem. Fill in the blanks with the definitions of each word (the Reader's Note should help you).

   distaff:

   flyers:

   spool:

   reel:

   quills:

   fulling mills:

   pink:

4. Below are two lists. The first one lists the parts of a spinning wheel Taylor refers to in his poem; the second one lists an element of spiritual life. Draw lines connecting them together to correspond to the way Taylor uses them in his poem.

reel	Thine ordinances
fulling mills	Thy holy Word
holy spool	my conversation
swift flyers	my soul
distaff	mine affections

5. What does Taylor ask God to do in the poem's final stanza?

Thinking About the Selection

6. Do you think Taylor's poem is addressed to a wrathful, vengeful God? Give reasons to support your answer.

Name Class Date

Upon What Base?
by Edward Taylor

Read the entire poem and answer the questions below.

1. What meaning of the word *globe* does Taylor have in mind?

2. Describe what a lathe does (if you don't know, look it up in the dictionary), and what it is doing in this poem.

3. What kind of industry do you think the words *bellows* and *cast* refer to in lines 3 and 4? What makes you think so?

4. When Taylor asks "Or whose command?" in line 5, who do you think he means? What makes you think so?

5. In lines 7 through 11, Taylor uses several images taken from sewing and clothmaking. Write them below.

6. What is the bowling ball in Taylor's metaphor in line 12?

7. A paradox is a statement that seems to say two opposite things. What is the paradox in lines 13 and 14?

8. In the final two lines of the poem, Taylor at last answers his question "Who? Who did this?" What is his answer?

Thinking About the Selection

9. What sense of God do you think Taylor communicates in this poem?

Name Class Date

To S. M., A Young African Painter on Seeing His Works

by Phillis Wheatley

Beginning the Selection

Read the title and the biography on page 70. Answer the questions below.

1. Name two things that the author of the poem and the person the poem is dedicated to, S. M., have in common.

2. What experience has prompted Wheatley to write this poem?

Continuing the Selection

Read the entire poem, and answer the questions.

3. Look up the words *lab'ring* (*laboring*) and *intent* in the dictionary. Several meanings of each are listed below. Check the one you think comes closest to Wheatley's meaning in the poem's first line.

lab'ring	_____	exerting the mind with strenuous effort
	_____	giving birth
	_____	suffering from some disadvantage
intent	_____	a state of mind in which an act is done
	_____	significance or meaning
	_____	a plan, or aim

4. What is Wheatley describing in the first six lines?

5. In the third line, Wheatley writes "When first thy pencil did those beauties give." What beauties does she refer to?

6. What does Wheatley recommend that S. M. do to achieve immortal fame in lines 7-10?

7. What is the "splendid city" mentioned in line 16?

8. Find another synonym between lines 15 and 20 used to describe the same thing.

Name Class Date

9. Wheatley uses a variety of words and phrases to evoke life on another plane. Make a list of all the ones you can find.

10. In lines 27-32, Wheatley imagines herself and S. M. in heaven. What is it like for them there?

11. Wheatley uses several images that evoke flying or release from the bonds of earth. List as many as you can find.

12. Sometimes eighteenth-century poets used complex wording to say something very simple. Think of simpler ways to say each of the following words.

thrice (line 15): ______

twice six (line 17): ______

pinions (line 25): ______

13. What words or phrases does Wheatley use that contrast with the brightness of heaven?

14. In the last line, what is the "fair creation"?

Thinking About the Selection

15. Wheatley never uses the word *freedom* in this poem, yet the idea of freedom is important to it. Make a list of the different kinds of freedom she alludes to.

Name Class Date

The Wild Honeysuckle

by Philip Freneau

Beginning the Selection

Read the biography on page 73, the title, and the entire poem. Answer the questions below.

1. The title and the poem's first stanza establish who or what the poem is addressed to, and where the poem is set. Fill in the blanks below:

   The poem is addressed to ______________________

   The poem is set in ______________________

2. What kind of growing conditions does the honeysuckle seem to prefer?

3. What circumstances does the honeysuckle avoid by growing where it does?

4. Based on information in this first stanza, if the honeysuckle were a person, what kind of person would it be? Write a short profile.

5. According to the poet, who created the honeysuckle and its environment?

6. What new information about the honeysuckle do you get in the second stanza? Does the honeysuckle seem any different to you?

7. In stanza 3, the poet writes of the flower's "future doom." What will happen to it?

8. What flowers does Freneau compare the honeysuckle to?

9. What two lines in stanza 2 foreshadow the tone of the third stanza? Give reasons to support your answer.

10. How does the poet feel in the third stanza?

11. What do you think the poet means by the lines "If nothing once, you nothing lose,/ For when you die you are the same"?

Thinking About the Selection

12. Do you think Freneau has only honeysuckle in mind in this poem? Use a separate sheet of paper to tell why or why not.

Name Class Date

Moral Perfection from The Autobiography

by Benjamin Franklin

Beginning the Selection

Read the title and the biography on page 78. Then read the selection to the end of the paragraph that begins "I determined to give a week's strict attention to each of the virtues successively," on page 80.

1. What does Franklin hope to attain? How does he define his goal?

2. What are some of the difficulties he encounters in achieving his goal?

3. What does the author conclude he must do to achieve his goal?

4. *Precept* means "a principle intended as a general rule of action." Five of the author's precepts are listed below. Use the blank next to each one to fill in the name of the appropriate virtue.

Think innocently and justly, and speak accordingly. ____________

Waste nothing. ____________

Let all things have their place. ____________

Avoid trifling conversation. ____________

Avoid extremes. ____________

5. Why doesn't Franklin attempt to master all the virtues at the same time?

6. Describe the method the author decides to use to work on each virtue.

Continuing the Selection

Read the rest of the selection, answering the questions below.

7. What virtue gives the author the most difficulty? Why?

8. What reasons does Franklin give to justify his inability to break some of his habits?

Thinking About the Selection

9. Pick four virtues you would choose to achieve moral perfection. On a separate sheet of paper, give a short precept for each one.

Name ______ Class ______ Date ______

A Witch Trial at Mount Holly

by Benjamin Franklin

Read the title and the entire selection. One belief commonly held about witches was that they were lighter than other people. The two tests of witches described by Franklin in this selection are attempts to prove that.

1. Answer the following questions:

What event is taking place in this selection? ______

Where is it happening? ______

When is the event taking place? ______

2. What are the accused charged with?

______

______

3. What tests are the accused going to be subjected to in order to determine whether they are witches?

______

______

4. To help prove their innocence, what demands do the accused make?

______

5. What were the results of the first test?

______

______

6. What were the results of the second test?

______

______

7. What was the response of the woman accuser who floated?

______

______

8. How did the accused man respond when he discovered that he floated?

______

9. What did the people watching think of the results?

______

______

______

Thinking About the Selection

10. Using this account as your guide, how do you think Benjamin Franklin felt about witch trials? Write your answer on a separate piece of paper.

Name Class Date

What Is an American?

by Michel-Guillaume Jean de Crèvecoeur

Beginning the Selection

Read the biography on page 87. Then read the selection to the bottom of page 88.

1. Crèvecoeur describes the American as "either an European or the descendant of an European." Can you think of a group or groups of people that Crèvecoeur did not include in this description?

2. The author believes that America supplies new prejudices for ones left behind. Where do these prejudices come from?

3. Which group of people does the author examine the closest?

4. According to Crèvecoeur, how do people resemble plants?

5. The author maintains that people are "nothing but" the air they breathe, their climate, government, religion, and their jobs. What important elements do you think Crèvecoeur has left off this list?

6. Crèvecoeur ends paragraph three with an apology. How does he consider himself inadequate to his task?

Continuing the Selection

Read the rest of the selection and answer the questions.

7. Describing the people who live by the sea, Crèvecoeur maintains that they are bolder and more enterprising than those who live inland. List a few of the examples he gives to support this contention.

Name ______ Class ______ Date ______

8. Below is a list of words used by Crèvecoeur when describing some of the characteristics of the people who live by the sea. Define each one in your own words, either as you understand it from the context in which it appears or by looking it up in the dictionary.

sagacious: ______

litigious: ______

censure: ______

disquisition: ______

uncurbed: ______

9. According to Crèvecoeur, how do people in the settlements that are farther inland differ from those on the coast?

10. In the author's view, what factors drive men to the woods? Use your own words.

11. Do you think Crèvecoeur holds the people of the woods in high esteem? Use evidence from the text to support your answer.

12. How do new frontiers get established, in the author's view?

13. What kind of man was Crèvecoeur's father?

14. What other identity besides that of "American" do immigrants acquire after they have settled in America?

Thinking About the Selection

15. Crèvecoeur compares human beings to plants in his essay. If you were to make a comparison like his, what would you compare people to? Make a list of the qualities the object you choose has in common with people.

Name Class Date

The Declaration of Independence

by Thomas Jefferson

Beginning the Selection

Read the title and the biography on page 92. Then read the selection through paragraph two, which ends with the line, "To prove this, let Facts be submitted to a candid world:"

1. What does the document's title tell you about its contents?

2. What are the political bands that Jefferson refers to?

3. Jefferson uses the word *station* in the first paragraph. What meaning of that word do you think he has in mind?

4. What do the "laws of Nature and of Nature's God" entitle everyone to, according to Jefferson?

5. What obligation to "the opinions of mankind" does Jefferson perceive?

6. What do you think "inalienable Rights" are? Look the words up in the dictionary if you don't know their meaning.

7. What are the "inalienable Rights" that Jefferson lists?

8. What other inalienable rights would you have included on the list if you had been the person writing it?

9. The three sentences below summarize three aspects of government that Jefferson touches on in paragraph two. Complete each sentence.

a. Governments are instituted to

b. Governments derive their just powers from

c. People have a right to

10. What tendency in regard to overthrowing oppressive governments does Jefferson observe from "experience"?

11. What is one duty the governed have, according to Jefferson?

12. What, according to Jefferson, has been the "direct object" of King George, ruler of Great Britain, toward the colonies?

Name Class Date

13. Look up the word *revolution* in the dictionary. What aspects of Jefferson's document identify it as a revolutionary document? Support your argument.

Continuing the Selection

Read the rest of the selection and answer the questions.

14. What kind of list does Jefferson compile in the second part of this document?

15. What rights did the King ask certain districts to give up in return for passing necessary laws?

16. What measures would the King take in order to force legislatures to do what he asked?

17. What does Jefferson claim the King has done to abdicate government? Look up the word *abdicate* if you don't know what it means.

18. Jefferson says that the colonists have "Petitioned for Redress." What does this mean? Look up the words if you don't know what they mean.

19. What exactly have the colonists done to try to alert the British to their point of view?

20. What is the tone of the last paragraph of the Declaration of Independence?

Thinking About the Selection

21. Imagine that you are King George reading this document for the first time. On a separate sheet of paper, describe your feelings.

Name Class Date

The Devil and Tom Walker

by Washington Irving

Beginning the Story

Read the biography of Washington Irving on page 109 and the title of this selection. Then read to page 111, column 2, to the end of the paragraph that begins "Let that skull alone!"

1. Where are the scattered oaks mentioned in the story located?

2. What three qualities made the inlet suitable for burying treasure?

3. What legendary figure buried treasure in this inlet, according to Irving. What happened to him after he buried the treasure?

4. What characteristic do Tom Walker and his wife share?

5. What quality does Irving emphasize when he describes the place Tom Walker and his wife live in? List some of the words Irving uses to build that effect.

6. Why do the "common people" have a bad opinion of the old fort Tom Walker stops at?

7. Describe the man seated on the tree stump opposite Tom.

Continuing the Story

Continue reading the story until the point where Tom sets up shop in Boston; stop at the end of the paragraph that begins "Thus Tom was the universal friend of the needy . . ." on page 116, column 1. Answer the following questions as you read along.

8. What parallels might be drawn between Deacon Peabody and the tree bearing his name?

9. What fate do you think is in store for the man named Crowninshield? Why?

Name Class Date

10. What names does the stranger go by? Who is he really?

11. What two events convince Tom Walker that the stranger is who he claims to be?

12. When Tom Walker refuses to accept the stranger's offer, his wife determines to find the stranger and accept the offer herself. What happens to her?

13. What is Tom Walker's major concern when his wife disappears?

14. When Tom searches for his wife and property at the Indian fort, what does he find tied up in her checked apron?

15. The stranger and Tom Walker finally do business with each other. What do you think the "one condition that need not be mentioned" is?

16. On what point does Tom Walker prove to be unusually squeamish?

17. How does Tom Walker become a "friend in need"? Is he really exhibiting friendship?

Continue reading until the end of the story.

18. How and why does Tom Walker attempt to cheat the devil?

19. What words of Tom Walker's bring the devil upon him?

20. How do the "good people of Boston" respond to Tom Walker's end?

Thinking About the Story

21. What point do you think Irving is making when he writes that all that was found in Tom Walker's coffers were cinders, chips, and shavings?

Name _______ Class _______ Date _______

A Rescue from The Deerslayer

by James Fenimore Cooper

Beginning the Story

Read the biography on page 119 and the title. Then read the selection to the end of the fourth paragraph.

1. What resolution does Deerslayer make in the first paragraph?

____

____

2. Describe the "entertainment" that the Hurons engage in with the Deerslayer.

____

____

____

3. What does the Huron chief, Rivenoak, fear will happen to the Deerslayer?

____

____

4. How do the Hurons react to the Raven's throw and the Deerslayer's response to it?

____

____

Continuing the Story

Read the story to page 122, column 2, through the paragraph that begins "You may call this shooting, Mingos . . . ."

5. The warriors who exhibit their skill in throwing the tomahawk have very different personalities. In the chart below, match the personal characteristics listed with the first initial of the appropriate name or names, if more than one apply. (R = Raven; M = Le Daim-Mose; BB = Bounding Boy)

pretentious	____	middle-aged	____
nervous/unsteady	____	intemperate	____
quiet	____	vain	____
good-natured	____	unskilled in the art	____
excitable	____	childish	____
confident	____	proud of his skill	____
hasty	____	brave	____
playful	____	hates the white man	____

6. Why is Bounding Boy rebuked for his throw?

____

____

Name Class Date

7. How do the Huron chief's hopes and the hopes of the rest of the tribe differ?

8. Why do you think the chief emphasizes the importance of skill in the next test of the Deerslayer?

9. Why is this second test a sterner proof of the Deerslayer's nerves than the first one?

Read the rest of the story through to the end.

10. The Deerslayer speaks in a form of dialect. Below is a list of some of the words in dialect that he uses. Fill in the blanks with the appropriate word in standard English.

ondo ____________ fa'an ____________

indivors ____________ arr'nd ____________

11. What other factor, besides the Deerslayer's taunt, makes the Hurons angry?

12. Although the Huron chief proposes that the Deerslayer be unbound to show "what his own body is really made of," releasing the prisoner has what other effect?

13. Who is Chingachgook? How does he penetrate the Hurons' sentinels?

14. What name does Briarthorn use to identify Chingachgook to the Hurons?

15. What event "saves" the Deerslayer and Chingachgook by providing a distraction?

16. What happens to the Hurons at the end of the selection?

Thinking About the Story

17. On a separate piece of paper, make a list of things the Deerslayer does to provoke the Hurons and play an active role in his escape.

Name Class Date

Thanatopsis

by William Cullen Bryant

Read the biography on page 128 and the title. Then read the entire poem. Answer the questions below.

1. To whom does Nature speak "a various language," according to the poet?

2. What do you think Bryant means by the words "visible forms"?

3. What does Nature offer to someone's "gayer hours"?

4. In contrast, what does Nature have to offer as a remedy for "darker musings"?

5. Bryant talks about "thoughts of the last bitter hour" in line 9. What do you think he means by this phrase?

6. Bryant shifts his focus in the next few lines and addresses someone by the pronouns "thy" and "thee." Who is addressing?

7. Beginning in line 10, the poet refers to a number of "sad images." In the list below, write your idea of what each one means.

   stern agony: __________

   shroud: __________

   pall: __________

   narrow house: __________

8. What effect do these "sad images" create, according to the poet?

9. What remedy does the poet offer for the blight that comes over the spirit?

10. What span of time does Bryant have in mind with the phrase "Yet a few days"?

Name Class Date

11. Rephrase the following sentence in your own words: "Thee the all-beholding sun shall see no more."

12. Bryant makes a sudden transition in mood from the end of the first section to the mood in this next section. What is that transition?

13. When the poet says that you will not "retire alone" in line 32, what does he mean?

14. Make a list of the decorations that make up the "mighty sepulcher."

15. In evoking the spirits of all those who have died, Bryant says they all rest in "the great tomb of man." What is he referring to specifically with this phrase?

16. What is meant, in lines 61 through 63, by "The gay will laugh/ When thou are gone, the solemn brood of care/Plod on . . ."?

17. What is the "innumerable caravan" in line 74? Can you find other phrases that have a similar meaning?

18. What advice does Bryant offer in the last section of the poem?

Thinking About the Selection

19. Did you find this to be a comforting poem? Why or why not? Use examples from the poem to help support your feelings.

Name Class Date

A Psalm of Life and The Children's Hour

by Henry Wadsworth Longfellow

A Psalm of Life

Read the biography on page 134 and the title of the poem. Then read the entire poem.

1. What does Longfellow not want to hear in the first stanza?

2. In stanza 2, the phrase "from dust to dust" is spoken of the body. How does the soul differ, in Longfellow's view?

3. In the next four stanzas, Longfellow makes suggestions about how to live. What are some of the things he thinks important?

4. In stanza 5, Longfellow refers to life as a bivouac, or army encampment. What, then, does the battleground represent?

5. In the final three stanzas, what can we all learn from great men, according to Longfellow?

The Children's Hour

This poem was written about Longfellow's three daughters, Alice, Allegra, and Edith.

1. What is the time of day in this poem?

2. The three children in the poem are all characterized by a word or phrase. How is each child described?

3. The poet calls his daughters "blue-eyed banditti," or robbers. What are they stealing from him? How is the narrator a "match" for the children?

Name Class Date

The Chambered Nautilus and The Ballad of the Oysterman

by Oliver Wendell Holmes

The Chambered Nautilus

Read the biography of Holmes on page 139 and the poem's title. Remember that the word *nautilus* comes from the Greek word *naus*, meaning "ship." Now read the poem.

1. What do the words "This is the ship of pearl" refer to?

2. In the first stanza the poet offers a series of images that evoke a certain setting. What is that setting? Make a list of the words that contribute to the poet's effect.

3. What phrase in the first stanza is a synonym for "ship of pearl"?

4. How is the first stanza different from the second?

5. What has happened to the ship of pearl?

6. What words does Holmes use in stanza 2 to give the impression of the nautilus as a delicate creature?

7. What is "the silent toil" the poet describes in stanza 3?

8. What fact do you learn about the chambered nautilus in this stanza?

9. Below is a list of phrases from the last two stanzas. Fill in the blanks with the meaning of each phrase.

   child of the wandering sea: ______

   leave thy low-vaulted past: ______

   leaving thine outgrown shell: ______

   by life's unresting sea: ______

Name Class Date

10. The poet finds a message in the life of the chambered nautilus. What is that message?

The Ballad of the Oysterman

Read the entire poem. Answer the questions below.

1. The setting of the poem and its two main characters are introduced in the first stanza. Fill in the blanks below for characters and setting, also giving the accompanying details that appear in the stanza.

Setting: ________

Characters: ________

2. Which character makes the first gesture? How is that gesture interpreted?

3. Why does the oysterman leave his skiff at home?

4. What allusion to Greek legend appears in the third stanza?

5. What happens in stanza 4 to make the oysterman jump back into the river?

6. The fisherman asks his daughter about the movement in the river as the oysterman swims away. What are the causes, according to her?

7. What happens when the fisherman calls for his harpoon?

8. What becomes of the two lovers in the last stanza?

9. Find several examples of inversion, or anastrophe, in the poem.

Name Class Date

from **Snowbound**

by John Greenleaf Whittier

Read the biography on page 144 and the title. Then read the entire poem. Answer the questions below.

1. What scene does Whittier describe in the first eight lines?

2. The sun provides the focus for these first lines. What kind of light does the sun give off?

3. The poet uses the words *portent* and *prophecy*. Look them up if you don't know what they mean. What event is prophesied in the first fourteen lines?

4. List several examples of inversion found in lines 1 through 18.

5. How do the first eighteen lines make you feel? List the words Whittier uses that cause you to feel this way.

6. Lines 18 through 30 give more information about the place the poem is describing. What more do you learn?

7. To whom does the pronoun *we* refer in these lines?

8. What event do lines 31 through 40 describe?

9. When the sun shines on the second morning, they see "a world unknown." Why does the poet describe it this way?

10. List the things that have taken on a new look, and what they now look like covered in snow.

11. The temperature of the last stanza is warm, in contrast to the cold of the first stanzas. What language does Whittier use to create that feeling?

Name Class Date

A Wish

by Fanny Kemble

Read the biography of Fanny Kemble on page 149 and the title of the poem. Answer the question below.

1. Make a list of several things you think the poem might be about before you read it.

Now read the poem. Answer the remaining questions.

2. What do you think the narrator's wish is after reading the poem?

3. What does the narrator mean by "Let me not die for ever . . ."?

4. What simile is used to describe how memory lives on? What does it mean?

5. What does the narrator ask for in lines 5 and 6?

6. What images does the narrator use to evoke feelings about death?

7. What is the one way the narrator doesn't want to be remembered?

8. What do you think the narrator implies with the words "Weep over those ye loved . . ."?

9. What does the narrator want for herself?

10. What kind of person do you think the narrator of this poem might be? Why?

Name Class Date

The Cask of Amontillado

by Edgar Allan Poe

Beginning the Story

Read the beginning of the story up to the place on page 152, column 1, where the narrator says, after persuading Fortunato to advise him about the Amontillado, "I suffered him to hurry me to my palazzo."

1. In the first line, the narrator tells us he has borne a thousand injuries from Fortunato "as best he could." What did Fortunato do that made the narrator finally vow revenge?

2. What does the narrator mean by "I must not only punish, but punish with impunity"?

3. The narrator doesn't ever tell Fortunato that he is angry at him. How does he act around Fortunato?

4. What is the one thing Fortunato and the narrator have in common?

5. Read the vocabulary note for the word *motley*. Why do you think the author has Fortunato dressed this way?

6. Look again at the dialogue between Fortunato and the narrator. How does the narrator persuade Fortunato to examine the Amontillado?

7. Do you believe the narrator is really concerned about Fortunato's health? Why or why not?

Continuing the Story

Continue reading until you come to the point on page 153, column 1, where the narrator says, "Be it so," and gives Fortunato his arm. Answer the questions below as you read along.

8. Montresor (the narrator) offers wine to Fortunato several times during their journey through the catacombs. Why do you think he does this?

Name Class Date

9. Catacombs are underground burial vaults. List several details of physical description about the catacombs.

10. What do you suppose Montresor will do with the trowel he shows Fortunato?

11. Here is a list of several personality traits. Which ones do you think best fit each character? Fill in the blanks with the character's name.

hasty: ______ manipulative: ______

deceitful: ______ clever: ______

greedy: ______ vain: ______

Continue reading until the end of the story.

12. What is the "ornamentation" in the crypt to which Montresor takes Fortunato?

13. What happens to Fortunato when Montresor shows him into the vault where he says the Amontillado is?

14. What does Fortunato do when he finally realizes what has happened?

Thinking About the Story

15. Several different settings in this story are listed below. Think about each one, then describe the mood in each place.

Montresor's deserted house:

crypt:

catacombs:

street at carnival:

Name Class Date

Hop-Frog

by Edgar Allan Poe

Beginning the Story

Read the title. Then read the selection through to the end of the paragraph on page 160, column 1, that ends when the narrator, talking about Trippetta's influence with the king, says "[She] never failed to use it, whenever she could, for the benefit of Hop-Frog."

1. Briefly describe the king and his chief pleasure in life.

2. What role did fools, jesters, and dwarfs play at the king's court? How do you feel this reflects on the king's character?

3. Describe Hop-Frog and Trippetta's friendship. What is it based on?

Continuing the Story

Read the story through to the end.

4. What "practical joke" does the king play on Hop-Frog?

5. What does Trippetta do to help Hop-Frog, and how does the king react?

6. What is the name of the "diversion" Hop-Frog comes up with?

7. Describe the effect the diversion, in its entirety, has on the masqueraders.

Thinking About the Story

8. What is Hop-Frog's motivation for the terrible trick he plays on the eight men?

Name Class Date

The Raven and Annabel Lee

by Edgar Allan Poe

The Raven

This is Poe's most frequently quoted poem. Listen closely to the rhythm, which helps create a feeling of mystery and sadness, as you read the entire poem.

1. Where does this poem take place? Give the location, month of the year, and time of day.

2. When the narrator opens the door to see what's outside, whose name does he whisper?

3. Who is Lenore?

4. Through what part of the room does the Raven enter?

5. What is the Raven's answer to each of the narrator's questions?

6. What effect do the Raven's answers have on the narrator?

7. Where is the Raven at the end of the poem?

8. What do you think the Raven represents in this poem? Explain.

Annabel Lee

Read the entire poem, listening for the rhymes, the rhythm, and the repeated words.

1. What facts does stanza 1 establish?

2. What kind of love do the narrator and Annabel Lee have for each other?

3. What happens to Annabel Lee? Who does the narrator blame, and why does he blame them?

4. How does the poet feel about Annabel Lee in the poem's present?

Name _______________ Class _______ Date _______

To Helen

by Edgar Allan Poe

Read the poem and then the Reader's Note on page 173. Answer the questions below.

1. Stanza 1 describes Helen's beauty. What is her beauty like to the poet? Use your own words to paraphrase the poet's words.

2. Find one example in this stanza of each of the poetic devices listed below.

   anastrophe: _______________ assonance: _______________

   _______________ alliteration: _______________

   _______________ simile: _______________

   rhyme: _______________ allusion: _______________

3. How does the poet characterize the sea in the first stanza as compared to the second?

4. What are three of Helen's characteristics that the poet mentions in the second stanza?

5. What are "Naiad airs" and "hyacinth hair"? (Hint: Check the Reader's Note.)

6. List three allusions that you can find in stanza 2.

7. Line 7 has several examples of assonance. List as many as you can find.

8. In stanza 3, how does Helen appear to the narrator?

9. Psyche is the personification of the soul in Greek mythology. How has Helen's effect on the narrator changed from the first stanza to the third?

10. List all the examples of assonance you can find in stanza 3.

Name Class Date

Stanzas on Freedom
by James Russell Lowell

Read the biography of James Russell Lowell on page 175, then read the entire poem. Answer the questions below.

1. Who is the first stanza addressed to?

2. What question does the poet ask his audience in this stanza?

3. What opinion do you think the poet has of slavery? What makes you think so?

4. What would make the mothers unfit to bear "the brave and free," according to Lowell?

5. What simile does Lowell use to describe the way blood rushes through the veins when one is aroused emotionally?

6. Stanza 3 goes on to describe true freedom. Make a list of the characteristics that define true freedom, according to the poem.

7. In stanza 4, the poet redefines what a slave really is. What is his new definition of a slave?

8. In the biography of Lowell, this quote is attributed to him: "I shall never be a poet till I get out of the pulpit." Pick any stanza, and tell why it seems to be written by one "in the pulpit."

Name Class Date

Escape: A Slave Narrative
by James W. C. Pennington

Beginning the Selection

Read the biography of Pennington and the title on page 177. Then read the selection through to the end of the paragraph that begins "I left this interesting young man . . . ", on page 180, column 1.

1. The narrator sets up the scene in the first paragraph. What do you learn about the events of the narration just from reading these first four sentences?

2. What are some of the obstacles standing in the way of the narrator's escape?

3. What could happen to the narrator should he be caught after trying to escape?

4. According to Pennington, what was the most annoying thing about slavery?

5. During the night, what is his guide to the North?

6. What advice does the friendly stranger have for the narrator? Does the narrator take it? Why or why not?

Continuing the Selection

Continue reading the story through to the paragraph that ends with the words "*See* how when he would do good, evil is thrust upon him . . .", on page 183, column 1.

7. Is the narrator happy to see the "Tavern"? Why or why not?

8. What are the papers that the man refers to when he questions the narrator?

Name Class Date

9. What about this incident provokes the narrator and makes him angry?

10. When seized by the four men, the narrator faces a dilemma, or what he calls "the pinch of the case." What is this dilemma?

11. Briefly describe the story the narrator tells the men at the tavern after being captured.

12. After he escapes again, the narrator delivers an apology and an explanation for his actions to the reader. What does he ask the reader to do?

Continue reading the story through to the end.

13. Make a list of the torments that lie ahead after the narrator's second escape.

14. What are the words that the narrator remembers whenever he is inclined to overlook the plight of the poor and wretched?

Thinking About the Selection

15. When James W. C. Pennington decides to escape, he must then determine whether or not to tell his family his plans. He decides not to; but what if he *had* let them in on his decision? Write a short account of the things his father, mother, sisters, and brothers might have said to him.

Name Class Date

Songs of America

Read the essay on page 186. Then read each selection all the way through and answer the questions before going on to the next.

Deep River

What are three of the features of this place called *home* mentioned in this spiritual?

Swing Low, Sweet Chariot

Read the Comment on Sorrow Songs by W. E. B. Du Bois on page 188. Then read the song entirely and answer the two questions below.

1. What do you think is meant by the word *home* in this song?

2. What do the singers of this poem look forward to?

Follow the Drinking Gourd

In this song, the "drinking gourd" is the Big Dipper, used as a guide to the North, and to freedom.

1. What are the two refrains in this poem?

2. All three spirituals recount journeys. How does the journey in this spiritual differ from that in the first two?

The Kansas Emigrants

by John Greenleaf Whittier

1. What comparisons does the poet draw between the emigrants and the Pilgrims?

2. What do you think the poet has in mind with the phrase "fraud of man"?

Clementine

1. Who is the narrator in this song?

2. How does he feel about his sweetheart's death?

Name Class Date

Maxims and Fable
by Ralph Waldo Emerson

Maxims
Read the biography of Emerson on page 204 and the Reader's Note on page 207. Then read the maxims, answering the questions below.

1. Read the first maxim. Look up the word *latent* if you don't know what it means. What does the author think will become of "latent" convictions?

2. Read the second maxim. What does Emerson mean by the words *society* and *manhood*?

   society: ______

   manhood: ______

3. Read the third and the eighth maxims. How are they similar?

4. Read the fourth maxim. What do you think Emerson means by the phrase "my life is for itself"?

5. Read the fifth maxim. What do you think the author has in mind when he uses the word *hobgoblin*?

6. What seems to be Emerson's opinion of the "statesmen and philosophers and divines" he writes about in maxim five?

7. Read the ninth maxim. Emerson uses specifics like *coach* and *feet* to make a more general statement. What is his point?

Fable
Read the entire poem, then answer the questions below.

1. Who called whom "Little Prig"?

2. The squirrel and the mountain possess different characteristics. List them below.

   squirrel: ______ mountain: ______

3. How does the squirrel regard its place in the world?

Name Class Date

from Self-Reliance: A Nonconformist, Traveling, and Reliance on Property
by Ralph Waldo Emerson

A Nonconformist

Read just the title and answer the question below.

1. Look up the word *nonconformist* in the dictionary. What kind of person do you think this selection will be about?

Now read the selection through to the end. Answer the questions that follow.

2. What does the author mean by the phrase "immortal palms"?

3. How does the author define right and wrong?

4. How does Emerson feel about "how easily we capitulate to badges and names"?

5. What does the author think he ought to say to the "angry bigot"?

6. What does Emerson mean by "Your goodness must have some edge to it"?

7. Under what circumstances will Emerson avoid company and his family?

8. For what kind of people does the author "grudge the dollar, the dime, the cent"?

9. List the charities Emerson rejects.

Name Class Date

Traveling

Read the selection through to the end. Answer all the questions below.

10. What reason does Emerson give for American's fascination with the "superstition of Traveling"?

11. Name the idols of the superstition of travel.

12. What do you think the author means by the phrase "The soul is no traveler"?

13. According to Emerson, how does the wise man behave when traveling?

14. List several good reasons for traveling, according to the author.

15. List three reasons people have for traveling that the author disagrees with.

16. What happens to people who travel just for amusement?

17. How does the traveler resemble ruins, according to Emerson?

18. In what way does the author find traveling to be a fool's paradise?

19. What do you think the word *giant* means in the last sentence? What other words does Emerson use that mean the same thing?

20. Think of a trip you made away from home. On a separate piece of paper, describe something about that trip to support the author's assertion that we bring our problems with us wherever we go.

Name Class Date

Reliance on Property

Read the selection through to the end. Then answer the questions below.

21. How does Emerson define reliance on property? What do you think he means?

22. What similarity can you find between a person who relies on property and a person who travels for amusement?

23. What point does the author make about the role of institutions in people's lives?

24. Why, according to Emerson, do people dislike assaults on institutions?

25. What kinds of property does a cultivated person hate?

26. What connection does the author draw between property and political parties?

27. How can people "instantly right" themselves?

28. Think of a specific action that might be considered an assault on each of the three institutions listed below.

church:

government:

school:

29. Do you think the author would agree with the maxim "There is strength in numbers"? Why or why not? Use the text to support your answer.

Name Class Date

from **The American Scholar: Man Thinking**

by Ralph Waldo Emerson

Read the title and the entire selection. Be aware that Emerson uses the word *Man* to mean human beings as independent individuals. Answer the questions below as you read.

1. What is the fable the author tells in the first paragraph? Where does it come from?

2. Why was Man divided into men, and what is this division compared to?

3. What must the individual do, according to the fable, in order to "possess" himself? What do you think the word *possess* refers to in this instance?

4. What is the "fountain of power"? What has happened to it? Use quotes from the text to support your answer.

5. What metaphor does the author use to describe society? What does this metaphor say about society?

6. Below is a list. Match the occupation with the part that the author contends each individual has become.

sailor	form
scholar	machine
attorney	dollars
farmer	rope
priest	intellect
tradesman	bushel and cart
mechanic	statute

7. In the degenerate state, what does the scholar become?

8. In what role can humankind find fulfillment?

Name Class Date

Brahma

by Ralph Waldo Emerson

Read the title and the headnote on page 212. The headnote gives important information that will help in understanding the poem. Read the entire poem, then answer the questions below.

1. Who is the poem's narrator? Who is the narrator addressing?

2. In the first stanza, the poet equates the slayer and the slain. What is the one thing both slayer and slain may not know?

3. What four paradoxes appear in stanza 2?

a.

b.

c.

d.

4. In setting forth these apparent contradictions, what point do you think the poet is trying to make?

5. How would you describe the poem's tone in stanza 3? Which line in this stanza do you think best expresses this tone?

6. What do you think the line "When me they fly, I am the wings" means?

7. What do the gods and saints pine for in stanza 4?

8. What does Brahma promise to the "meek lover of good"?

9. Many of Emerson's readers found this poem very shocking. Why do you think this poem was seen as undermining conventional religious beliefs?

Name Class Date

Days

by Ralph Waldo Emerson

Read the title and review the headnote on page 212. Answer all the questions below after reading the entire poem.

1. What or who are the daughters of Time?

2. How does Emerson personify Days?

3. Emerson describes Days as hypocritical, probably because they offer so much and often leave us with so little, but why do you think he also describes the Days as "muffled and dumb"?

4. The poet also compares Days to dervishes. Look the word up if you don't know what it means. What quality of time does this description capture?

5. How do the Days march in?

6. Why do you think the Days carry diadems (crowns worn by royalty) and fagots (bundles of twigs tied together and used for fuel) in their hands?

7. To whom do the Days offer their gifts? What are those gifts?

8. The list of things the Days offer begins with the ordinary—bread—and progresses to the most transcendent—the sky. In quickly taking herbs and apples, which is the speaker choosing?

9. What do you think the narrator means by the words "I . . . forgot my morning wishes"?

10. How does the Day respond to the narrator's choice? Why?

11. On a separate piece of paper, write a maxim that summarizes the point of this poem.

Name Class Date

The Snowstorm

by Ralph Waldo Emerson

Read the title and the entire poem. Be sure to read the poem's footnote. Answer all the questions below.

1. How does the snow arrive?

2. Inversion is used in the first three lines. Write the lines as they would appear normally.

3. What image does the phrase "the whited air" evoke?

4. List everything in the first stanza that has been hidden by snow.

5. What circumstance concludes the first stanza?

6. What example of personification can you find in the second stanza?

7. Who is the "fierce artificer" in the second stanza?

8. What does the artificer create?

9. What quality does the poet ascribe to the wind's "wild work"?

10. List some of the North Wind's fanciful handiwork.

Name ______ Class ______ Date ______

from **Walden: Why I Went to the Woods** and **Why I Left the Woods**

by Henry David Thoreau

Why I Went to the Woods

Read the biography of Thoreau on page 216. Then read the selection through to the end, answering the questions below.

1. List several of the reasons the author gives for going to the woods.

2. What uncertainty about life do most people experience?

3. Why do you think the author emphasized the words *somewhat hastily?*

4. Name two similes found in the second paragraph.

5. What recommendations does Thoreau give for simplifying life?

6. Near the end of this essay, Thoreau moves from the personal to the political. He finds the nation overgrown, unwieldy, and ruined by luxury. What does he suggest as a cure?

7. What national advances does Thoreau deem unnecessary?

8. What do you think Thoreau meant by the sentence "We do not ride on the railroad; it rides upon us. . . ."?

9. Do you know anyone who needs to simplify his or her life? Write a short profile of someone who fits Thoreau's description.

Name Class Date

Why I Left the Woods

Read the selection to page 220, to the end of the paragraph that begins "There was an artist in the city of Kouroo . . . ." Answer the questions below as you read.

1. What reason does Thoreau give for leaving the woods?

2. What experience in the woods supports the author's observation that the ruts of tradition and conformity are very deep? What analogy does he draw?

3. In the previous selection, "Why I Went to the Woods," the author urges his readers to simplify, simplify, simplify. What lesson about simplicity did Thoreau learn in the woods?

4. What should the person who "hears a different drummer" do, according to Thoreau?

5. What does the artist in the city of Kouroo hope to attain in making his staff?

6. What happened to the artist's friends while he searched for the right wood with which to make his staff?

7. What effect does the artist's search for perfection have on time?

Continue reading the selection through to the end.

8. Thoreau's prose is studded with maxims. Find two in the next paragraph.

9. What benefits does the author claim are to be found in poverty?

10. Thoreau compares the hospitality of a king and of a man who lived in a tree. Whose company did he prefer?

11. What extended metaphor appears in the next to last paragraph?

Name Class Date

from **Civil Disobedience**
by Henry David Thoreau

Beginning the Selection
Read the selection through the paragraph that ends "Moreover, any man . . . constitutes a majority of one already," on page 225. Answer the questions below as you read.

1. What kind of government does the author like the best?

2. What is Thoreau's opinion of the Mexican War?

3. How does government affect trade and commerce, according to Thoreau?

4. How can citizens obtain the kind of government that will command their respect?

5. Under what circumstances does Thoreau urge breaking the law?

6. To what course of action does Thoreau urge all Abolitionists?

Continuing the Selection
Continue reading the selection through to the end, answering the questions below.

7. How many people does it take to resist slavery for slavery to be abolished, according to Thoreau?

8. When Thoreau is put into prison for not paying his taxes, how does he see himself, the State, and the people outside the prison walls?

9. What qualities must a truly free and enlightened state have?

Thinking About the Selection
10. Thoreau believed that the individual was more important than the State. On a separate piece of paper, explain why you agree or disagree.

Name ______ Class ______ Date ______

This Sacred Soil

by Chief Seattle

Beginning the Selection

Read the biography on page 229. Then read the selection to the point where Chief Seattle says, "Our dead never forget the beautiful world that gave them being . . ." on page 230. Answer all questions.

1. What is the occasion of this speech?

2. What do you think Chief Seattle's feelings are on this occasion?

3. What does Chief Seattle promise the "Big Chief at Washington"?

4. What images does Chief Seattle use to describe his people and the Big Chief's people?

5. Why does Chief Seattle say, "Your God loves your people and hates mine"?

6. What three differences between the red and white peoples does Chief Seattle describe?

   a. ______

   b. ______

   c. ______

Continuing the Selection

Read the rest of the selection, answering the questions below.

7. What prediction does Chief Seattle make for his own people?

8. What prediction does he make for the white people?

9. Why will the white people never be alone, according to Chief Seattle?

10. What does Chief Seattle say about death?

Thinking About the Selection

11. Chief Seattle says, "the White Man . . . cannot be exempt from the common destiny." On a separate piece of paper, discuss that destiny.

Name Class Date

from **Loom and Spindle**

by Harriet Hanson Robinson

Beginning the Selection

Read the title and the biography on page 232. Then read the selection to page 233, column 2, where the author writes ". . . the corporation went on cutting down the wages."

1. What status did factory women have, according to the author?

2. Why were high wages offered to women?

3. Why did the first strike take place?

4. What singular event caused "surprise and consternation" among the audience listening to speeches?

5. What event caused the author to feel great pride?

6. What event does the author look forward to as another moment that will occasion a similar sense of pride?

7. Why is Harriet's mother turned away from her boardinghouse?

Continuing the Selection

Read the rest of the selection, answering the questions below.

8. Describe *The Lowell Offering*. Who wrote it, and how much did it cost?

9. What good effect on its readers does Robinson ascribe to *The Lowell Offering*?

Thinking About the Selection

10. Imagine that you are someone who is in Harriet Robinson's situation at the Lowell cotton mills. Would you have gone out on strike? Explain why or why not on a separate piece of paper.

Name Class Date

Young Goodman Brown

by Nathaniel Hawthorne

Beginning the Story

Read the biography on page 236 and the Reader's Note on page 246. Then read the selection to page 239, column 1, where the traveler says, "Be it so. Betake you to the woods, and let me keep the path." Be aware that *Goodman* and *Goody* are forms of address, like *Mr.* and *Mrs.*

1. The first three paragraphs set up the main points of the story. Fill in the blanks below with the appropriate information about the item at left.

   characters: ______________________ setting: ______________________

   time of day: ______________________ event: ______________________

2. What elements of the paragraph beginning "Poor little Faith!" alert the reader to the nature of Goodman Brown's errand?

3. Goodman Brown meets a man along the lonely, wooded path. Do they meet by chance? Explain.

4. Briefly describe the man Goodman Brown meets.

5. What remarkable thing does the traveler carry with him?

6. What does Goodman Brown tell "he of the serpent" about his father, grandfather, and ancestors?

7. What does his companion tell Goodman Brown about these same people?

8. What is Goodman Brown's reaction when he learns of all the people who are "firm supporters" of his companion?

9. Why do you suppose the traveler laughs so heartily at Goodman Brown's fear of meeting his minister's eye at church?

Name Class Date

10. Why does Goodman Brown go into the woods when he sees Goody Cloyse on the path?

11. Who do you think the traveler is?

Continuing the Story

Continue reading the story to page 243, column 1, where the "dark figure" welcomes his children, saying, "Ye have found thus young your nature and your destiny. My children, look behind you!"

12. What does Goodman Brown discover about Goody Cloyse from his hiding place in the woods?

13. As Goodman Brown sits contemplating his decision to return to Faith's arms, two riders pass by. Who are they?

14. While looking up to heaven, Goodman Brown sees a black cloud overhead. He hears many voices, among them what he thinks is Faith's voice. What does he then see that causes him to say, "Come, devil; for to thee is this world given"?

15. Describe Goodman Brown's state of mind as he sets off again into the forest.

16. Name four people Goodman Brown sees, or thinks he sees, beneath the blazing fire.

Continue reading the story through to the end.

17. The devil prepares to "lay the mark of baptism" on Goodman Brown and his wife. In doing so, what will they be taking part in?

18. Goodman Brown calls out to Faith to look up to heaven and resist "the wicked one." Where does he then find himself?

19. How does Goodman Brown's state of mind change after the night he spends in the forest?

Summarizing the Story

20. On another piece of paper, list the main events as they happened in the story.

Name Class Date

What Redburn Saw in Launcelott's-Hey

by Herman Melville

Beginning the Story

Read the biography on page 248. Then read the selection to page 250, column 2, where the porter asks, . . . "do you suppose, that Parkins and Wood want their warehouse turned into a hospital?"

1. After reading the headnote, title, and first paragraph, fill in the blanks below with the correct information.

   Name of city: ______

   Name of street: ______

   Name of narrator: ______

   Name of narrator's boardinghouse: ______

2. From the narrator's description of his discovery, you get a feeling of what the tone of the selection will be. What is the tone?

______

3. What do you learn immediately about the narrator's character?

______

______

4. What kind of response does the narrator get from the people he asks for help?

______

______

Continuing the Story

Continue reading the story through to the end.

5. How is Handsome Mary's response like everyone else's? How is it different?

______

______

6. After the narrator finally succeeds in getting food for the woman and children, how does he feel about having helped them?

______

Thinking About the Story

7. The narrator ends with the reflection ". . . are we not like people sitting up with a corpse, and making merry in the house of the dead?" Write a few lines describing something you think this sentiment applies to today.

______

______

______

______

______

______

Name Class Date

from **Hospital Sketches**

by Louisa May Alcott

Beginning the Selection

Read the biography on page 254. Then read this excerpt from Alcott's journal until you come to page 256 of your book, the end of the paragraph that begins "*January*, 1863 *Union Hotel Hospital, Georgetown, D.C.*"

1. As Louisa Alcott writes her first journal entry in 1862, why are nurses needed in Washington?

2. Why does Alcott decide to become a nurse?

3. What is Mrs. Alcott's response to Louisa May's departure?

4. Describe a few of the things Alcott experiences on her first day as a nurse.

5. What is it about John Sulie that so impresses Louisa May Alcott?

Continuing the Selection

Continue reading the selection through to the end, answering the questions below.

6. What opinion does Alcott have of the men and women she works with? Use the text to support your answer.

7. Why does Alcott finally leave the hospital?

Thinking About the Selection

8. Using information gathered from the selection, on a separate sheet of paper write a brief portrait of the author as though you were one of her patients writing in a journal.

Name Class Date

from **Uncle Tom's Cabin**

by Harriet Beecher Stowe

Beginning the Story

Read the biography on page 259. Then read the story to page 262, column 1, through the end of the paragraph that begins "A few last words and tears, a few simple adieus . . . ."

1. What has Eliza heard at the Shelby's door?

2. What does she resolve to do?

3. Who does Eliza tell about her plans?

4. What reason does Uncle Tom give for staying behind?

5. What message does Eliza leave for her husband?

Continuing the Story

Continue reading the story through to the end, answering the questions below.

6. Why does Eliza think it is unlikely that people will think that she is running away?

7. What prevents Eliza from attaining her goal?

Thinking About the Story

8. How do you think Mrs. Shelby will react when she reads Eliza's letter?

Name ______ Class ______ Date ______

from What the Black Man Wants

by Frederick Douglass

Beginning the Selection

Read the biography on page 266. Then read the selection to page 267, column 1, through the paragraph that ends "Hence, I say, now is the time to press this right."

1. Douglass says that he is for the "immediate, unconditional, and universal enfranchisement" of the black man. Define the words below.

   immediate: ______

   unconditional: ______

   universal: ______

   enfranchisement: ______

2. According to Douglass, if the black man is not a voting citizen, he is still a slave. Who, then, is his master?

3. What objections to immediate enfranchisement are cited by the speaker? Do you think he agrees that these objections should be taken seriously?

4. What does Douglass feel will happen if Abolitionists fail to press for their cause now?

Continuing the Selection

Continue reading the selection through to the end, answering all the questions.

5. How does Douglass feel about suffrage for women?

6. Douglass states that if black men are denied suffrage, they are being declared "unfit to exercise the elective franchise." What does he say this leads to?

7. Douglass doesn't want sympathy, benevolence, or pity. What does he want?

8. The narrator answers the question "What shall we do with the Negro?" What does he think should be done and why?

9. What metaphor does Douglass use to illustrate his point about noninterference?

Thinking About the Selection

10. One of the "inalienable rights" named in the Declaration of Independence is liberty. In this speech, Douglass rejects the idea of liberty as a "privilege." On a separate piece of paper discuss the difference between "rights" and "privileges."

Name ____ Class ____ Date ____

Ain't I a Woman?

by Sojourner Truth

Read the biography on page 270. Then read the selection through to the end.

1. When Sojourner Truth says, ". . . where there is so much racket there must be something out of kilter," what do you think she means?

2. Whose clamor for rights is putting white men "in a fix"?

3. What view of women do you think men had, judging from Sojourner Truth's words?

4. Why was Sojourner Truth never lifted over puddles, helped into carriages, or given the best place?

5. Sojourner Truth uses specific examples from her own life to contradict the argument that women are helpless. What are these examples?

6. How does the speaker dismiss the argument that women lack the intelligence of men?

7. How does Sojourner Truth handle the argument that Christ wasn't a woman, therefore women don't deserve the same rights men do?

8. Who is Sojourner Truth alluding to when she mentions "the first woman God ever made"?

9. Discuss what you feel makes this an effective speech.

Name Class Date

Gettysburg Address

by Abraham Lincoln

Read the biography on page 271. Then read the selection through to the end, answering the questions below.

1. The first paragraph of the address describes the "new nation." What two aspects of that new nation does Lincoln choose to emphasize?

2. What does the civil war test, according to Lincoln?

3. What did the people who died at Gettysburg give their lives for?

4. What is the unfinished work of which Lincoln speaks?

5. Who really consecrated the ground at Gettysburg, according to Lincoln?

6. What task do the living have now, in Lincoln's view?

7. List the four resolves Lincoln considers the most important to be drawn from Gettysburg.

8. Imagine that you are at Gettysburg and have just heard Lincoln's address. Write a short paragraph describing your impressions of his two-minute speech. Include a reference to the tone of his address.

Name ____ Class ____ Date ____

Letter to His Son

by Robert E. Lee

Read the biography on page 273. Then read the selection through to the end, answering the questions below.

1. In the first paragraph, Lee writes, "How his spirit would be grieved . . . ." To whom is Lee referring?

2. What do you think Lee means by the words "the wreck of his mighty labors"?

3. What is the state of the country, according to Lee?

4. What word does Lee use to describe the actions of the North towards the South? What does the word mean?

5. What is the very worst thing that could happen to the country, according to Lee?

6. What is the one thing Lee will not sacrifice in attempting to preserve the Union?

7. What view does Lee hold of secession, and for what reasons?

8. What kind of government does Lee say the "patriots of the Revolution" would have established if any member of the confederacy could secede at will?

9. Do you think Lee wants a war to happen? Support your answer.

10. What would Lee do if the Union were dissolved?

11. What is the only case in which Lee says he would fight?

Name Class Date

Song of the Chattahoochee

by Sidney Lanier

Read the biography on page 275. Read the entire poem, then read it again aloud. Answer the questions below.

1. The "I" of the poem is the Chattahoochee River. Where is it hurrying to?

2. What is the tone of the first stanza? Make a list of the words that contribute to this tone.

3. Find three examples of alliteration in stanza 1.

4. What is the river being urged to do in stanza 2, and by whom?

5. List two phrases in stanza 3 that contribute to the mood of quiet and security.

6. Find as many examples of internal rhyme as you can in stanza 3.

7. What does the river encounter in stanza 4, and what do these things do?

8. What do "the voices of Duty" call the Chattahoochee River to do?

9. What does the river do in the plain?

10. Who or what is calling the Chattahoochee in the last two lines?

Name Class Date

from Uncle Josh's Zoo: The Ant
by Josh Billings

1. What virtues does the author see in ants?

2. In this portrait, the author is really describing the opposite characteristics of another species. Who or what is he actually describing?

3. Take the fifth paragraph and rewrite it as if it were a portrait of human weaknesses.

4. What point do you think the author wants to make when he writes "I shall sell out my money and real estate"?

Tall Tale
Davy Crockett

1. What is Davy Crockett doing at the time of this tale?

2. Why does the raccoon come down from the tree?

3. What point about himself was Crockett trying to make with this tale?

4. Think of something you do especially well. Write a short tall tale about that thing.

Brag
Mike Fink

1. What area of the world is the narrator's territory?

2. What two larger-than-life claims does the narrator make for himself?

3. Think of something you have to brag about. Write a sentence that makes a larger-than-life claim about your particular skill.

Name Class Date

I Hear America Singing and There Was a Child Went Forth

by Walt Whitman

I Hear America Singing

Read the biography on page 294 and the essay on Whitman and Dickinson on page 295. Then read entire poem. Answer the questions below.

1. What words does the poet use to characterize the mechanics' song?

2. What does the carpenter do while he sings? What does the mason do?

3. Where does the deckhand sing his song? Where does the shoemaker sing his?

4. What makes each worker's song different from any other?

5. What is the poem's last image?

There Was a Child Went Forth

Read the entire poem, answering the questions below.

1. Who is the poem's central character? What does this character do?

2. What kinds of images does the poet use in lines 5-8?

3. List the people the poet mentions in lines 14-18.

4. Who are all these very different people?

5. How is the mother depicted?

6. How is the father described?

7. What things become part of the child in lines 33-38?

Name Class Date

When Lilacs Last in the Dooryard Bloom'd

by Walt Whitman

Read the Comment on page 309. Then read the entire poem, answering the questions below.

1. Who is Whitman mourning in this elegy?

2. In Section 1, the poet introduces three images, which are listed below. Fill in the blanks next to each image with the word or words used to modify each.

lilac:

star:

spring:

3. The trinity referred to in Section 1 comprises the lilac, the western star, and the poet's memory of Abraham Lincoln. In the first line of Section 2, the western star now represents a person. Who?

4. What mood does Section 2 evoke?

5. How does the mood of the poem change in Section 3?

6. List some of the words the poet uses in Section 4 to describe the thrush.

7. The speaker identifies with the hermit thrush singing "Death's outlet song . . . ." What kind of song do you think a song from a "bleeding throat" would be?

8. What is the event that takes place in Section 5?

9. What time of year is it? What details does the poet supply to let you know?

10. In Section 6, the poet uses language to create an aura of darkness. Make a list of the words the poet uses to do this.

11. The poet reintroduces the image of the sprig of lilac that he picked in Section 3 at the end of Section 6. Why do you think he does this?

Name Class Date

12. In Section 7, the speaker offers to cover death with roses and lilies. What does this indicate concerning his feelings about death?

13. In Section 8, the speaker addresses the "western orb," the planet Venus, also called the evening star. What emotion does the speaker ascribe to it?

14. The "singer bashful and tender" referred to in Section 9 was mentioned in a previous section. Who or what is it?

15. What parallel does the speaker draw between himself and the "singer" in Section 10?

16. In Section 11, what pictures does the speaker of the poem decide to hang on the walls of the burial house?

17. In Section 11, the sun is described as "gorgeous" and "indolent." How is the sun described in Section 12?

18. Section 13 is a transitional section in which the speaker finds consolation in the song of the thrush. Compare Section 13 to Section 2.

19. In Section 14, the speaker surveys all the activity that surrounds him—the tides, the teeming cities, etc.—then retreats to the woods. What does he hear there?

20. Who does the thrush sing to (in italic type)? Is it a song of lament?

21. How do you think the speaker now sees death? Support your answer with lines from the text.

22. In Section 15, Whitman uses images of the battlefield to show that death is not always unwelcome. Who really suffers, according to the poet?

23. Section 16 concludes by returning full circle to the place where the poem began. What images does the poet use here that originally appeared in the preceding sections?

Name Class Date

What Is the Grass? from **Song of Myself**
by Walt Whitman

Read the entire poem and answer the questions below.

1. Who asks the question, *"What is the grass?"*

2. What is the poet's first response to the question?

3. Below is a list of symbols the poet associates with the grass. Next to each word, write in other words or phrases Whitman uses to describe each association.

flag of my disposition: ________

handkerchief of the Lord: ________

a child: ________

a uniform hieroglyphic: ________

4. How does the poet shift the focus of the poem in lines 12 through 24?

5. In these lines, the poet names all of the places the grass might have sprung from. Make a list of those places.

6. What natural phenomenon do you think the poet refers to in lines 12 through 24?

7. How does the poet answer his question "What do you think has become of the young and old men . . . of the women and children?"

8. What does the poet use as proof of his assertion that there is no death?

9. What conclusion about death does Whitman draw?

10. What do you think the poet's mood is when he contemplates death? Explain.

Name Class Date

Bivouac on a Mountain Side, When I Heard the Learn'd Astronomer, and Sparkles from the Wheel

by Walt Whitman

Bivouac on a Mountain Side

Read the entire poem and answer the questions below.

1. What does the title tell you about the poem? Look up the word *bivouac* if you don't know what it means.

2. What does the poet see in line 1?

3. Lines 2 through 4 describe the setting in greater detail. What new details does Whitman supply?

4. What time of day is described in the poem? List the words or phrases that tell you this.

When I Heard the Learn'd Astronomer

1. Read the entire poem. Who is the subject, and what is he interested in?

2. What effect does the lecture have on the speaker?

3. How does the poem's speaker choose to refresh himself?

4. What contrast can you find in the way the stars or heavens are treated in the beginning lines and in the ending lines of the poem?

Sparkles from the Wheel

1. Read the entire poem. What alliteration can you find in the first line?

2. What scene does the poem's speaker stop to watch?

3. List some of the details of the scene that "seize" the speaker.

Name Class Date

The Soul Selects Her Own Society and **My Life Closed Twice Before Its Close**

by Emily Dickinson

The Soul Selects Her Own Society

Read the biography on page 315 and the essay on Whitman and Dickinson on page 295. Then read the entire poem. Answer the questions below.

1. In stanza 1, what meaning do you think the poet has in mind when she uses the word *society*?

2. What two things does the soul do?

3. In stanza 2, who or what does the soul watch coming to her door? What do you think they symbolize?

4. How does the soul respond to these callers?

5. In stanza 3, what does the soul do after choosing one?

6. Name the poetic device Dickinson uses in representing the soul.

My Life Closed Twice Before Its Close

Read the entire poem, then answer the questions below.

1. What paradox does the poet introduce in the first line of the poem?

2. Make a list of all the different meanings you can think of that the poet might have in mind when she uses the word *close*.

3. What is the speaker of the poem waiting to see?

4. What do you think the poet has in mind in the "third event"? Why do you think so?

5. The poet ends the poem with yet another paradox. What is it?

Name Class Date

I Felt a Funeral in My Brain

by Emily Dickinson

This poem is thought to portray the speaker's mental deterioration—ending in a complete breakdown of reasoning power. Read the entire poem, listening for the repetitive, hard-edged words that help give the poem its impact.

1. The first line describes an event and the place where the event happens. What are they?

Event: ______________________ Setting: ______________________

2. Line 2 continues the description by adding what new detail?

3. Why do you think the poet repeats the word *treading* twice in line 3?

4. The word *Service* in stanza 2 refers to a religious rite. What effect does this service have on the poem's speaker?

5. In stanza 2, the speaker repeats the word *beating*. What word does this remind you of in stanza one?

6. Do you think stanza 2 creates a new mood or continues to build on the mood in stanza 1? List your reasons.

7. In stanza 3, the poet writes "With those same Boots of Lead." What image in stanza 1 does this phrase expand on?

8. What word in the first line of stanza 4 continues the image used in the last line of stanza 3?

9. In the third line of stanza 4, the poet talks about "some strange Race." What meaning of the word do you think she has in mind?

10. How does stanza 4 differ from the other three stanzas?

11. What is the thing that breaks in stanza 5?

12. Do you agree that the speaker has emotional problems? Use examples from the poem to support your argument.

Name Class Date

Some Keep the Sabbath Going to Church and "Faith" Is a Fine Invention

by Emily Dickinson

Some Keep the Sabbath Going to Church

Read the entire poem, then answer the questions below.

1. What is the subject of the poem?

2. What do others do to keep the Sabbath? What does the speaker do?

3. Look up the word *chorister* if you don't know what it means. Who or what is the chorister at the speaker's church service?

4. List the words in stanza 2 that have to do with the church.

5. Do you think stanza 2 continues the theme of the first stanza or establishes a new theme? Explain your reasoning.

6. In stanza 3, the speaker once again compares herself to people who go to church. What do you think she perceives the difference between them to be in this stanza?

"Faith" Is a Fine Invention

Read the entire poem, then answer the four questions below.

1. This poem contrasts religion and science. What words does the poet use to represent each?

   religion: ______________ science: ______________

2. Which do you think the poet views as the more trustworthy, religion or science? Explain your reason for thinking so.

3. Why do you think Dickinson emphasizes the word *see*? What do you think she means by the word?

4. Try writing the idea expressed in this poem in your own words.

Name Class Date

There's a Certain Slant of Light

by Emily Dickinson

The following poem describes the speaker's reaction to a light she finds oppressive. Read the entire poem, and answer all the questions below.

1. What time of year and time of day are the setting for this poem?

2. What mood is established in stanza 1?

3. What does the poet compare this mood to?

4. Find an example of alliteration in stanza 1.

5. Stanza 2 speaks of a "Heavenly Hurt" that leaves no scar. Where might that hurt be? What makes you think so?

6. Find an example of assonance in this stanza.

7. Check the phrase below that you feel best defines the meaning of "None may teach it," found in the first line of stanza 3.

   _____ Each must experience it personally

   _____ No one can train it to be something else

8. In the third stanza the slant of light is described as "the Seal Despair" and "An imperial affliction." Where does it come from?

9. What happens to the landscape when the light falls over it?

10. List the words the poet uses throughout the poem to create a feeling of majesty about the suffering felt?

11. What parallels can be drawn between the images of death in this poem and winter?

Name Class Date

I Heard a Fly Buzz When I Died

by Emily Dickinson

This poem depicts a deathbed scene in which all are gathered to witness the speaker's death. The poem reverses a conventional attitude of Dickinson's day, which held that the moment of death was a spiritually significant event. The visitors often waited expectantly for the dying one to bring them word from the beyond. Read the Reader's Note on page 326 before reading the entire poem.

1. What is happening to the speaker of the poem?

2. What atmosphere does the poet create in the first stanza?

3. Find an example of onomatopoeia in this stanza.

4. In stanza 2, the speaker focuses outward, looking around the room. Who or what does she see?

5. What metaphor does the poet use to refer to the act of dying in this stanza?

6. Who or what do you think the poet means when she refers to "the King"?

7. In stanza 3, what actions has the speaker already taken?

8. What happens in stanza 3 just as everyone waits for the dying speaker to see "the light" (and perhaps give them a clue to the beyond)?

9. What effect does the fly have on the quiet, dignified scene?

10. What do you think the phrase "the Windows failed" represents in the last stanza? Why?

11. Why do you think the poet chose the common housefly as the central symbol in this poem?

12. What paradox ends the poem?

Name Class Date

Because I Could Not Stop for Death

by Emily Dickinson

This poem takes us on what seems to be a rather carefree ride with kindly Mr. Death. But is it? Read the entire poem, then answer the questions below.

1. Death stops for the speaker. What do they do next in stanza 1?

2. What poetic device is used to represent death?

3. Who else is in the carriage with them?

4. How does the poet establish a sense of time in stanza 2? What words does she use to create this sense?

5. What do they pass as they ride?

6. What do you think the journey in stanza 3 represents?

7. In stanza 4, the speaker, now even beyond the setting sun, grows cold. Why?

8. The poet portrays the next stage of the journey in stanza 5. What do you think the "House" represents?

9. They only "pause" at this House. Where do you suppose they go from there?

10. In the last stanza, the poet twists time around. What effect does this stanza have on your idea of time in the poem?

11. The poet uses the words "kindly" and "Civility" in reference to Death. Do you think she really means that death is kind? Why or why not?

Name Class Date

The Celebrated Jumping Frog of Calaveras County

by Mark Twain

Beginning the Story

Read the Comment on page 334. Then read the story to page 332, column 2, through to the end of the paragraph that begins "Smiley said all a frog wanted was education . . . ."

1. What does the narrator of the story suspect his friend's motive was in referring him to Simon Wheeler with an inquiry about Leonidas W. Smiley?

2. Briefly describe Simon Wheeler's appearance and his surroundings.

3. What is singular about the manner in which Wheeler tells his tale?

4. What is Jim Smiley's most outstanding characteristic?

5. What wager does Smiley offer Parson Walker before he has a chance to think about what he is saying?

6. What special characteristic did Smiley's old nag exhibit during horse races?

7. What caused Andrew Jackson to lay down and die?

8. What was the only thing a frog needed, according to Smiley?

9. What human qualities does the narrator ascribe to Dan'l Webster?

Continuing the Story

Continue reading to the end, answering the questions below.

10. What does the stranger do to the frog to gain an advantage over Smiley?

11. What new story does Simon Wheeler begin to tell? How does the narrator react?

Thinking About the Story

12. Do you think that Smiley deserved to be tricked? On a separate piece of paper, tell why or why not.

Name Class Date

To Be a Steamboatman from Life on the Mississippi

by Mark Twain

Beginning the Story

Read the story to page 336, column 1. Stop at the paragraph that begins "My father was a justice of the peace . . . ." Answer all the questions below.

1. What ambition did the narrator share with all his friends?

2. How does the author characterize his village before the arrival of the steamboat?

3. How does the village change when the steamboat arrives?

4. Twain's description of the steamboat creates an exciting visual picture. Some of the phrases below are used in this description, some are not. Check those that are.

____ a gigantic mast hung with bright banners ____ gorgeous paddle boxes ____ a glass and gingerbread pilot house ____ a gilded rudder ____ a big bell ____ a fenced and ornamented texas deck ____ state rooms magnificently appointed ____ a gangplank over the port bow ____ two tall chimneys puffing black smoke

Continuing the Story

Continue reading the story to the end, answering the questions below.

5. List some of the things the boy who becomes an apprentice engineer does to make the other boys despise him.

6. What happens that gives this boy even more renown?

7. What results did the career of this one steamboatman have on the rest of the boys in the village?

8. Is the narrator successful in finding a job on a steamboat?

Thinking About the Story

9. On a separate piece of paper, describe a deeply felt ambition that you have had. What did you do in order to achieve that ambition? Was someone else able to achieve it before you were?

Name Class Date

Shenandoah

Anonymous

Read "American Voices" on page 340 and the definition of *ballad* at the back of your book, if you haven't done so already. Then read the entire selection. Note that all lines that are not quoted are the narrator's.

1. What is the mighty river's name?

2. What is located on the borders of the river?

3. Two lines of each stanza are a refrain. What are they?

4. Whose voice do you think addresses Shenandoah in the third stanza?

5. What does the voice in this stanza threaten to do?

6. In stanza 4, what does the trader offer Shenandoah in exchange for his daughter?

7. What is Shenandoah's response to the trader?

8. Who is the next man to seek Shenandoah's daughter?

9. Who is speaking in the final stanza? Explain.

10. In the last stanza of the ballad, the word *bound* takes on a new meaning. How does it differ from the way it was used in the preceding stanzas?

11. What role does dialogue play in this ballad?

Name Class Date

El Corrido de Gregorio Cortez

Anonymous

Read the essay titled "American Voices" on page 340 and the Comment on page 342. Then be sure to read the definition of *ballad* in the Handbook of Literary Terms at the back of the book. Finally, read the entire selection.

1. What event is described in the first stanza?

2. Who is the man who killed the Major Sheriff?

3. What do the rangers use to chase Cortez?

4. What simile is used in stanza 3 to describe the difficulty in catching Gregorio Cortez?

5. What motivation do the rangers who are chasing Cortez have in pursuing him?

6. How many people are pursuing Cortez? What does he manage to do even though they have cornered him?

7. Why do you think the Major Sheriff doesn't want to kill Cortez?

8. How does Cortez respond to the Major Sheriff's plea?

9. What are Cortez's last words in the ballad?

10. In what way is Cortez the underdog?

11. How does "El Corrido de Gregorio Cortez" conform to the tradition of ballads?

Name Class Date

My Heart Feels Like Bursting

by Satanta

Read the biography of Satanta on page 343. Then read his speech, answering the questions below.

1. How does Satanta feel about the land?

2. What doubts does Satanta have about the men who speak for President Andrew Johnson?

3. Why do you think that Satanta doesn't want what he calls medicine lodges—white people's churches and schools—in his country?

4. Why don't Satanta and his people want to go to the reservation?

5. What does Satanta see when he goes up the river?

6. Imagine that you are being forced to leave your home. Write a few sentences describing your feelings when you see strangers using—and destroying—your things.

I Will Fight No More Forever

by Chief Joseph

Read the biography of Chief Joseph on page 345. Then read his speech, answering the questions below.

1. What is the condition of Chief Joseph's people?

2. How would you describe Chief Joseph's feelings about his people?

3. How would you describe Chief Joseph's state of mind in this speech?

Name Class Date

The Outcasts of Poker Flat

by Bret Harte

Beginning the Story

Read the biography on page 346. Then read the selection to page 349, column 1, through the paragraph that begins "There was a remembrance of this in his boyish and enthusiastic greeting of Mr. Oakhurst."

1. What had changed in Poker Flat over the night?

2. Describe Mr. Oakhurst's character and reputation.

3. What are the arguments posed by the townspeople for and against hanging Oakhurst?

   For: Against:

4. In addition to Mr. Oakhurst, who are the other Poker Flat outcasts?

5. The four stop at noon, after the Duchess declares she cannot go on. What reasons for continuing the journey does Oakhurst give?

6. Why is Tom Simson John Oakhurst's "devoted slave"?

Continuing the Story

Continue reading to the end, answering the questions.

7. Does Mr. Oakhurst want Tom and Piney to remain at the camp?

8. Tom and Piney decide to stay with the others, and they all bed down for the night. Who is missing the next morning?

9. When Oakhurst returns to camp after searching for the trail, he hears laughter. What does he fear this means, and what is really going on?

10. Beginning on the third night, Tom, the Innocent, narrates a famous story. What is the story, and who is "Ash-heels"?

11. What happens to Mother Shipton, Piney, and the Duchess?

Thinking About the Story

12. On a separate piece of paper, tell why you think Mr. Oakhurst kills himself.

Name ______ Class ______ Date ______

An Occurrence at Owl Creek Bridge

by Ambrose Bierce

Beginning the Story

Read the biography on page 355. Then read the selection through to the end of Section II.

1. Briefly describe the setting and situation of the story in the first paragraph. Include as many details as you can.

______

______

2. What does the author's description tell you about the character of the man who is being hanged?

______

______

3. How is the hanging to be carried out?

______

______

______

4. Is the man who tells Farquhar that the Owl Creek bridge would "burn like tow" a Union or Confederate soldier?

______

Continuing the Story

Continue reading the story through to the end.

5. What unexpected event occurs near the beginning of Section III?

______

6. The author uses the physical senses—sight, sound, and feeling—to describe Farquhar's impressions once he has removed the rope from his hands and neck. Fill in the list below with language the author uses for each sense.

Sight: ______

______

______

Sound: ______

______

______

Feeling: ______

______

______

Thinking About the Story

7. As Farquhar is about to hold his wife he feels a blow to his neck, then everything goes dark. What has happened?

______

Name Class Date

A New England Nun

by Mary E. Wilkins Freeman

Beginning the Story

Read the biography on page 364. Then read the story through to the end of the paragraph on page 367, column 1, beginning "If he could have known it, it would have increased his perplexity and uneasiness . . . ."

1. What mood does the author create in the first paragraph?

2. The author uses Louisa's actions to define her character. Pick one of Louisa's actions in paragraphs two through four and write a brief description of Louisa's character as it is revealed by those actions.

3. Reading the scene where Joe Dagget visits Louisa, what do you think Louisa's feelings for Joe are? Joe's for Louisa?

4. What do you think Louisa's action in sweeping up after Joe symbolizes?

Continuing the Story

Continue reading to the end of the story.

5. What change came over Louisa after her mother and brother died, and she was left alone?

6. What two activities will Louisa miss most when she leaves her home and goes to live with Joe and his mother?

7. How do Caesar's circumstances in life resemble Louisa's? How do they differ?

8. What qualities do Lily Dyer and Joe Dagget reveal in the conversation between them overheard by Louisa?

Thinking About the Story

9. Do you think Louisa will be happy with her decision? Explain why or why not on a separate piece of paper.

Name Class Date

A Pair of Silk Stockings

by Kate Chopin

Beginning the Story

Read the biography on page 374. Then read the selection to page 376, column 2, through the paragraph that begins "Mrs. Sommers after that did not move in the direction of the bargain counter." Answer the questions below.

1. What matter is occupying Mrs. Sommers's mind at the start of this story?

2. What does Mrs. Sommers decide to do with this windfall?

3. Does Mrs. Sommers think back often to the "better days"? Why or why not?

4. How is it that Mrs. Sommers finds herself sitting at a counter where silk stockings are being displayed?

5. What are Mrs. Sommers's thoughts about having bought the pair of silk stockings?

Continuing the Story

Continue reading the story through to the end, answering the questions.

6. What is it about Mrs. Sommers that confuses the clerk in the shoe department?

7. After buying the boots, what other pleasures does Mrs. Sommers indulge in?

8. Why do you think Mrs. Sommers wishes that the cable car would go on forever?

Thinking About the Story

9. Have you ever spent money on something that you hadn't planned to? Write a short paragraph on a separate piece of paper describing your purchase and how it made you feel afterwards.

Name ______________________________ Class ______________ Date ______________

Of the Meaning of Progress

by W.E.B. Du Bois

Beginning the Selection

Read the biography on page 379. Then read the selection to page 381, column 1, through the paragraph that begins "There they sat, nearly thirty of them. . . ." Answer the questions below.

1. Where and at what time of year does this selection take place?

____

2. The author meets Josie and her family. How is Josie special?

____

3. Describe the condition of the school in which the author is to teach.

____

____

4. What is Josie's great ambition?

____

5. Below is a list of the students in the author's school. Fill in the blanks beside their names with a few of the descriptive words the author uses.

Josie: ______________ Martha: ______________

Fanny: ______________ 'Thenie: ______________

'Tildy: ______________ Ruben's girl: ______________

6. When the attendance of the school slips, the author sets out to find out what is keeping students from school. List two of the reasons.

____

____

Continuing the Selection

Continue reading the selection through to the end.

7. The author spends Friday nights with various students and their families. Which family is his favorite?

____

8. How did the people in the community who had experienced slavery differ in their outlook from those who hadn't?

____

____

9. Ten years later the author returns to the community where he taught school. What has become of those listed below?

Josie: ______________ Martha: ______________

Jim: ______________ Ben: ______________

'Tildy: ______________ Ella: ______________

Thinking About the Selection

10. Du Bois's young students are people he obviously cares deeply about. On a separate piece of paper, write a descriptive essay about someone you care about.

Name Class Date

An Episode of War
by Stephen Crane

Beginning the Story
Read the biography on page 386. Then read the selection through to the end of the paragraph on page 388, column 1, that begins "And the men in silence stared at the wood, then at the departing lieutenant . . . ."

1. What is the lieutenant doing when the story opens?

2. What happens to him?

3. How do the men and the lieutenant respond to the incident?

4. How do the men act toward the lieutenant after he is injured?

5. Why do you think that the lieutenant goes off by himself?

Continuing the Story
Continue reading the rest of the story, answering the questions below.

6. How does his wound alter the lieutenant's perception of the activities around him?

7. How does the officer who wraps the lieutenant's arm make him feel?

8. Describe what is happening as the lieutenant arrives at the field hospital.

9. What is the one thing the lieutenant wants to do to involve himself in this scene?

10. How does the manner in which the surgeon treats the lieutenant differ from the way in which his fellow soldiers treated him?

Thinking About the Story
11. On a separate piece of paper, explain why you think the lieutenant says of his lost arm, "I don't suppose it matters so much as all that."

Name Class Date

I Met a Seer, A Man Said to the Universe, and The Wayfarer

by Stephen Crane

I Met a Seer

1. Read the entire poem. What is a seer? What does the seer hold in his hands?
2. What demand does the speaker in the poem make of the seer?
3. Why do you think the seer lets the speaker in the poem see the book of wisdom?
4. What kind of a person do you think the speaker is?
5. What do you think has caused the speaker to go blind?

A Man Said to the Universe

1. Read the entire poem. What does the man say to the universe?
2. What does the universe's response to the man signify?

The Wayfarer

1. Read the entire poem. What is the feeling the wayfarer has when he sees the pathway to truth?
2. What does the wayfarer conclude about the condition of the pathway to truth?
3. What two things about the pathway to truth are different than the wayfarer expected?
4. Why does the wayfarer give up his journey over the pathway of truth?
5. What kind of a person do you think the speaker in this poem is?

Name ____ Class ____ Date ____

Sympathy

by Paul Laurence Dunbar

Read the biography on page 392, then read the entire poem and answer the questions below.

1. The first line of the poem gives us an image of confinement—the bird in the cage—what image is presented in the next six lines?

2. What mood does this imagery create? How does the image of the caged bird affect this mood?

3. Find examples of assonance in the first stanza.

4. How does the imagery in the second stanza contrast with the imagery in the first stanza?

5. Find an example of consonance in the second stanza.

6. What do you think Dunbar means by the phrase "old, old scars"?

7. What is it about the bird's song that the speaker thinks people are in danger of misunderstanding?

8. Find an example of alliteration in the third stanza.

9. What does the caged bird represent?

10. Why do you think Dunbar titled his poem "Sympathy"?

Name ______________________ Class ________ Date ________

Miniver Cheevy and Richard Cory

by Edwin Arlington Robinson

Miniver Cheevy

Read the biography on page 394 and the entire poem, including the footnotes. Then answer the questions below.

1. What do you learn about Miniver Cheevy in the first stanza?

2. What does Miniver Cheevy love?

3. What places are mentioned in the third stanza, and what do they represent?

4. Miniver mourned romance and art, and loved the Medici. What did he curse?

5. What does Miniver Cheevy do about the unhappiness he feels?

Richard Cory

Read the entire poem, then answer the questions below.

1. What did Richard Cory look like, according to the first two stanzas?

2. What kind of personality did he have?

3. What effect did he have on the townspeople?

4. Robinson writes that Richard Cory was "richer than a king." What other words does the poet use to elevate Cory above the townspeople?

5. What happened "one calm summer night"? Why is this phrase ironic?

Name Class Date

Lucinda Matlock and Richard Bone

by Edgar Lee Masters

Lucinda Matlock

Read the biography on page 396 and the entire poem. Answer the questions below.

1. How did Lucinda Matlock amuse herself before she was married?

2. Even though she was happily married, Lucinda Matlock experienced sadness in her life. What do you think caused her sadness?

3. Lucinda Matlock kept house, tended the sick, and gardened. What did she do for the sheer pleasure of it?

4. What caused Lucinda Matlock's death?

5. How does Lucinda Matlock's tone change at the end of the poem? Why do you think her tone changes?

Richard Bone

Read the entire poem, then answer the questions below.

1. What does Richard Bone do?

2. What information was Richard Bone ignorant of when he first came to Spoon River?

3. What does Richard Bone learn the longer he lives in Spoon River?

4. What kind of person do you think Richard Bone was?

Name Class Date

Mrs. Charles Bliss
by Edgar Lee Masters

Read the entire poem, then answer the questions below.

1. Why do Mrs. Charles Bliss and her husband remain together even though both of them wanted a divorce?

2. Who is advised by whom?

3. How do the children feel about their parents?

4. The poet uses repitition to create a mood. What is that mood?

5. According to Mrs. Charles Bliss, what damage was done to the children because of this situation?

6. What two analogies does the narrator draw to the circumstances under which her children were raised?

7. What does Mrs. Charles Bliss think about the advice the preacher and the judge gave to her and her husband?

8. What are her feelings towards the men who gave the advice?

9. Imagine that Mrs. Charles Bliss has come to you asking for advice. Write a short paragraph outlining what you would tell her to do.

Name ________ Class ________ Date ________

A Wagner Matinée

by Willa Cather

Beginning the Story

Read the biography on page 412. Then read the title and the selection to page 414, column 2, through the paragraph beginning "From the time we entered the concert hall. . . ."

1. What recollection comes to the narrator's mind when he learns that his Aunt Georgiana is coming to visit?

______

2. Where have his aunt and uncle lived for the past thirty years?

______

3. In what ways has Aunt Georgiana helped the narrator?

______

4. Where does Clark take Aunt Georgiana in the afternoon?

______

5. Clark is afraid his aunt will be painfully embarrassed in this unfamiliar setting. Is she? Explain.

______

Continuing the Story

Read the story through to the end, answering the questions.

6. The narrator describes the parts of the orchestra that are listed below. Fill in the blank to the right of each with the adjective or phrase the narrator uses to describe it.

musicians: ______ instruments: ______

linen: ______ fiddle necks and bows: ______

coats: ______ ______

7. What is Aunt Georgiana's initial reaction to the *Tannhaüser* overture?

______

8. During the *Tristan and Isolde* prelude, Aunt Georgiana sits staring at the violin bows. What simile describes the movement of the bows?

______

9. How does Aunt Georgiana respond during the piece from *The Flying Dutchman*?

______

10. Who was the "tramp cowpuncher"? What did he bring to Georgiana's life?

______

______

11. What words does Aunt Georgiana speak at the end of the concert?

______

Thinking About the Story

12. Do you think Aunt Georgiana will return to the homestead? On a separate piece of paper, explain why or why not.

Name Class Date

Sophistication

by Sherwood Anderson

Beginning the Story

Read the biography on page 421. Then read the selection to page 423, column 1, through the paragraph that begins "When the moment of sophistication came to George Willard. . . ."

1. What event opens the story?

2. What details does the author give about the ways in which the town "worked terribly at the task of amusing itself"?

3. Who is the main character? What is he doing when the story opens?

4. George is about to leave Winesburg. Where does he plan to go, and what does he plan to do there?

5. What has happened in George Willard's life that may account for his feeling old and tired?

6. In paragraph five, Anderson asserts that a boy may cross into manhood when he first does what?

7. What is "the sadness of sophistication" described by the author in this same paragraph?

8. What does George Willard think about and want most during this moment?

9. What does George Willard want to show Helen White now?

Continuing the Story

Continue reading the story through to the paragraph that begins "At the upper end of the fairground, in Winesburg, there is a half-decayed old grandstand," on page 426, column 1.

Name ______ Class ______ Date ______

10. The paragraph beginning "As for Helen White, . . ." signals a shift in the point of view to Helen White's perspective. Who is she with, and what is she thinking about?

11. What similarity exists between the feelings of George Willard and those of Helen White?

12. How has Helen White changed recently?

13. The author uses a flashback in this story. What information does the flashback give us about Helen and George?

14. How does George Willard feel about the way he had behaved in Helen White's company? Why does he feel this way?

15. Briefly describe the street scene as George Willard stands in the doorway waiting. How does it make him feel?

16. What happens just before George Willard decides to go see Helen?

17. A shift in the point of view turns the story back to Helen White. Briefly describe where she is, who she is with, what her emotions are, and what she finally does.

Continue reading the story through to the end.

18. Helen and George sit in the grandstand of the deserted fairground. What others, according to Anderson, are also present?

19. Why does George come to feel "renewed and refreshed"?

20. What do Helen and George do to "relieve their embarrassment" at having kissed?

Thinking About the Story

21. On a separate piece of paper, write a short paragraph describing George and Helen's behavior the next time they meet. Use dialogue.

Name Class Date

The Jilting of Granny Weatherall

by Katherine Anne Porter

Beginning the Story

Read the biography on page 429. Then read the selection through the paragraph that begins "I want you to pick all the fruit this year . . ." (page 432, column 2).

1. What is the setting of the story, who is the main character, and what is the main character's situation?

2. Below is a list of sentences. Some are spoken by Granny Weatherall, some by Doctor Harry, and some are thoughts that go through Granny Weatherall's mind. Fill in the blanks next to each sentence with the speaker's name.

   "I'd have you respect your elders, young man." ________

   ". . . you're going to be good and sorry." ________

   "The brat ought to be in knee breeches." ________

   "We'll have you up in no time." ________

   "I'll call for you when I want you." ________

3. What are Granny Weatherall's parting words to Doctor Harry after his first visit?

4. What imagery does Katherine Anne Porter use to describe Granny Weatherall drifting off after Doctor Harry leaves?

5. What aspects of Cornelia's character can be understood from Granny Weatherall's thoughts about her?

6. What metaphor does Porter use to describe "the plan of life"?

7. How does the author describe the thoughts of death that come to Granny Weatherall?

8. How did Granny Weatherall manage to "get over the idea of dying"?

Name Class Date

9. Why would Granny Weatherall's husband, John, not recognize her if he saw her?

10. List some of the things that Granny Weatherall remembers doing by herself.

Continuing the Story

Continue reading the story through to the space on page 435, column 1. Answer the questions below.

11. What memory comes over Granny Weatherall in the paragraph that begins "The pillow rose about her shoulders and pressed against her heart . . ."?

12. How many years has it been since she waited for the man who never came?

13. The Doctor returns and gives Granny a hypodermic. Why do you think Granny then speaks of ants?

14. What metaphor does the author use to describe memory?

15. What does Granny Weatherall want to tell George? Who is George?

16. Who is it that catches Ellen as she faints on her wedding day, promising, "I'll kill him for you"?

17. What do you think the sentence "Don't lay a hand on him, for my sake leave something to God" refers to?

Continue reading the story through to the end.

18. To what does Porter compare Cornelia's voice, and what happens to it near the end of the story?

19. How does the author describe the moment of Granny Weatherall's death?

Thinking About the Story

20. On a separate piece of paper, write about Granny Weatherall as though you were her daughter Cornelia.

Name Class Date

Winter Dreams

by F. Scott Fitzgerald

Beginning the Story

Read the biography on page 437. Then read the selection through to the end of Section I on page 440. Answer the questions as you read.

1. How does Dexter Green differ from many of the other caddies at the golf course?

2. What does Dexter's father do?

3. Briefly describe some of Dexter Green's fantasies.

4. What is the reason Dexter gives Mr. Jones for quitting caddying?

5. Describe the flashback that appears in Section I of the story. What purpose do you think it serves?

6. Why does Dexter really quit caddying?

Continuing the Story

Continue reading the story through to the end of Section II. Answer the questions as you read.

7. What have Dexter Green's "winter dreams" persuaded him to do at the start of Section II?

8. What does Dexter do to make money when he has finished college?

9. What is the occasion for Dexter's second meeting with Miss Jones?

10. What sort of character does Miss Jones have, as revealed by this incident? Has she changed since Dexter first met with her? Explain.

Name Class Date

11. What is Mr. Hedrick's opinion of Judy Jones?

12. What is Dexter's mood later in the evening as he lies on the spring-board listening to the sound of the piano?

13. What reason does Judy Jones give for leaving the man who has come to see her?

Continue reading the story to the end. Answer the questions below.

14. What is it that Dexter believes careless dress requires?

15. Judy Jones confesses to Dexter that she has suffered a disappointment. What is that disappointment?

16. What "beautiful and romantic thing" does Judy say to Dexter?

17. What does Dexter Green discover about Judy Jones's social life?

18. What does Dexter do eighteen months after becoming involved with Judy?

19. When he visits the University Club, who does Dexter meet, what do they do, and what does his companion propose?

20. What does Dexter feel about the reactions of others to his throwing over Irene for Judy?

21. What surprising news does Devlin bring Dexter?

Thinking About the Story

22. When he hears what has happened to Judy, Dexter Green cries for himself rather than for her. Why?

Name Class Date

In Another Country

by Ernest Hemingway

Beginning the Story

Read the biography on page 453. Then read the selection through to the end of the paragraph on page 455, column 1, that begins "There were three boys who came each day who were about the same age as I was."

1. With what imagery does the author choose to open the story?

2. How does the narrator get warm on his way to the hospital?

3. Why are the men at the hospital every afternoon?

4. Briefly describe the ailments of the narrator and the major.

5. What sports did each of the two men—the narrator and the major—once play?

6. How does the major feel about his prospects for recovery?

7. What kind of response did the men get as they went to the café after they were done at the hospital?

Continuing the Story

Continue reading the story to page 455, column 2, through the paragraph that begins "The three with the medals were like hunting hawks . . . ."

8. Why does the boy with the black silk bandage not have any medals?

9. How does the narrator describe the emotions of the men who all go to the café together?

10. What do the men have in common?

11. Why was the narrator given his medals?

Name Class Date

12. Why did the others get their medals?

13. What knowledge does the narrator gain of himself when he thinks of doing the things the other men had done to get their medals?

14. What metaphor does Hemingway use to distinguish between the narrator as a soldier and the other men?

15. How does the friendship between the men change after the episode of the medals?

Continue reading the story through to the end.

16. What study does the major encourage the narrator to take up?

17. How does the narrator's view of the Italian language change?

18. What reason does the major give at first when he says, "A man must not marry"?

19. Why is the major really so agitated at the thought of the narrator's wanting to marry?

Thinking About the Story

20. Briefly describe the mood of this story. Give examples to support your impressions.

Name Class Date

The Bear

by William Faulkner

Beginning the Story

Read the biography on page 459. Then read the story to the end of the paragraph on page 462, column 2, that begins "How?" the boy said. "How will he know—"

1. What is the legend that the boy has listened to for years?

2. What happened for two weeks in November and June, and had happened for as long as the boy could remember?

3. Faulkner writes that men fear the wilderness. In what ways is the bear like the wilderness? Use the text to support your answer.

4. At the end of paragraph four, the author uses the phrase "the yearly pageant of the old bear's furious immortality." What is he referring to?

5. How old is the boy when he goes to the camp for the first time?

6. What is different about the sound of the dogs when they are on the trail of the bear?

7. What name does the boy call the bear?

8. Why does the bear come into camp every year, according to Sam Fathers?

9. How is the dog with the torn ear like "folks," according to Sam?

10. When Sam and the boy find the bear's claw marks in a log and its footprints in the earth by the log, what realization does the boy come to about the bear?

11. According to Sam, what are the only ways the bear can be killed?

Name Class Date

Continuing the Story

Continue reading the story through to the paragraph that begins "Then he saw it again," on page 466, column 2.

12. What kind of relationship do you think the boy has with Sam?

13. Briefly describe the boy's first encounter with the bear.

14. What four things does the boy leave behind to more completely feel a part of the wilderness?

15. Describe the boy's second encounter with the bear.

16. What metaphor does Faulkner use to describe the bear's departure from the glade?

17. How does the boy change between his second encounter with the bear, when he is eleven, and his fourteenth year?

Continue reading to the end of the story, answering the questions.

18. Describe the dog that the boy takes with him to hunt the bear.

19. When the boy realizes that the dog is going to attack the bear, what does he do?

20. What does the boy's father do when he learns that the boy had a chance to kill the bear, but didn't?

21. After the boy's father speaks, the boy thinks about the four characters in the drama. List those four players and describe their roles.

Thinking About the Story

22. Imagine that you are the boy, just returned from the last hunting trip. On a separate sheet of paper, write a letter to a close friend explaining why you did not shoot the bear.

Name Class Date

The Leader of the People

by John Steinbeck

Beginning the Story

Read the biography on page 471. Then read the selection to the point where Jody says, "I guess I'll just do it then," on page 474, column 2.

1. What are Billy Buck and Jody doing when the story opens?

2. How are the mice in the haystack personified?

3. What piece of information do you learn about Carl Tiflin, Jody's father, in the exchange between Jody and Billy Buck?

4. The letter that Carl Tiflin brings to the house has the information in it that Jody's grandfather is coming to visit. In the blanks below, fill in the reaction of each person to this news.

   Jody:

   Mrs. Tiflin:

   Carl Tiflin:

5. What explanation does Mrs. Tiflin give for her father's fondness for the past?

Continuing the Story

Continue reading the story through to the end of the paragraph that begins "Jody exchanged a secret and satisfying look with Grandfather," on page 478, column 2.

6. List several of the arresting images the author uses in the next two paragraphs to describe the things Jody sees while walking to meet his grandfather. What mood is established?

7. Briefly describe the grandfather. What information about his character does the description of him give? Use the text to support your answer.

8. What is the first thing Jody asks his grandfather to do?

Name Class Date

9. What news about the ranch does Jody have to tell his grandfather?

10. How does Carl Tiflin respond to Grandfather's stories?

11. How does Jody's mother react to her husband's comments?

12. What do you think Jody feels about his father's response to Grandfather? Use the text to support your answer.

Continuing the Story

Continue reading the story through to the end. Answer the questions.

13. What does Jody think about when he goes to bed that night? What understanding of himself does he have?

14. What is Jody all excited about the next morning?

15. What thought of Billy Buck's "staggers" Jody?

16. What do you think is the tone of Carl Tiflin's comment, "A man that's led a wagon train across the plains has got to be pretty careful how he dresses"?

17. What is Grandfather's response to the remark of Carl's that he overhears when he comes into the kitchen for breakfast?

18. What does Grandfather really want people to feel when he tells his stories?

Thinking About the Story

19. When Grandfather tells Jody, "But that's not the worst—no, not the worst. Westering has died out of the people," he's admitting that he is a man whose time has come and gone. In what way is Carl Tiflin better suited to the present time?

Name Class Date

The Man Who Saw the Flood

by Richard Wright

Beginning the Story

Read the title and the biography on page 482. Then read the selection to page 484, column 2, the sentence that reads "He stood looking at the mud-filled fields."

1. Who are the main characters first introduced in the story?

2. What are the circumstances in their lives at the start of the story?

3. List the conditions that the family finds on their farm when they return to it.

4. What simile does the author use when referring to the flood mark on the walls of the cabin?

5. What positive aspects does the family discover at their farm?

Continuing the Story

Continue reading to the end of the story, answering the questions.

6. Who is Burgess? Why is Tom reluctant to go to him for help?

7. What will happen to the family if they try to run away?

8. What do they discover on the shelf the flood didn't reach?

9. What do you think May feels about the prospect of Tom going back to Burgess?

10. What is Burgess's response to Tom's request to "knock something off" the debt, since he is "down n out"? Is he sympathetic to Tom's plight? Explain.

Thinking About the Story

11. Why do you think Tom doesn't respond gratefully to Burgess's offer to stake him and his family to grub? Write your answer on another sheet of paper.

Name Class Date

A Worn Path
by Eudora Welty

Beginning the Story
Read the biography on page 488. Then read the selection to page 491, column 2, through the paragraph that begins "Phoenix heard the dogs. . . ."

1. Briefly describe the woman named Phoenix Jackson.

2. Below is a list of several of the obstacles Phoenix comes across in her journey. In the space provided, fill in a sentence of dialogue that Phoenix speaks in response to each of the obstacles.

   path runs up a hill: _____

   caught in thorns: _____

   log laid across the creek: _____

   buzzard: _____

   scarecrow: _____

3. List two things that Phoenix hallucinates during her journey.

4. What simile does Welty use to describe the boarded up cabins that Phoenix passes?

5. What simile does Welty use to describe Phoenix falling into the ditch after she swipes at the black dog?

6. What does Phoenix do to distract the hunter from the nickel he has dropped?

Continuing the Story
Continue reading to the end of the story, answering the questions.

7. What request does Phoenix make of a woman on the street?

8. Where is it that Phoenix Jackson has been heading all this time?

9. What is wrong with Phoenix's grandson?

10. What is Phoenix going to do with the ten cents she now has?

Thinking About the Story
12. Write a paragraph or two on a separate sheet of paper describing the scene when Phoenix Jackson returns home with her present.

Name Class Date

The Garden

by Ezra Pound

Read the short biography of Pound on page 496. Then read the entire poem, answering the questions below.

1. What simile does the poet use for the woman in the first stanza?

2. Where does the poem take place?

3. What is the woman dying of, and how?

4. Who else is in the park along with the woman?

5. Make a list of the contrasts the poet accentuates between the woman and the "rabble."

6. What kind of character do you think Pound creates in the woman, based on the images that he presents?

7. What do you think the poet means by the line "In her is the end of breeding"?

8. What is the woman almost afraid of, according to the speaker?

9. Why does he think she wants someone to talk to her?

Thinking About the Poem

10. Rewrite the poem's first and third stanzas from the woman's point of view, using your own imagery to describe her perception of things. The man might be sitting on a park bench, watching her.

Name Class Date

The River-Merchant's Wife: A Letter
by Ezra Pound

Read the entire poem, then answer the questions below.

1. What information does the image "While my hair was still cut straight across my forehead" convey?

2. Who are the two main characters in the first stanza? What do they do?

3. How did the two main characters feel about each other then?

4. How does their relationship change in stanza 2?

5. How does the narrator of the poem change between stanzas 2 and 3?

6. What is the central event of the last stanza?

7. What is the mood of this stanza? What images establish the mood?

8. What meaning do you think the narrator ascribes to the growing of the mosses that have become too deep to be cleared away?

9. What hurts the narrator? Why do you think she is hurt?

10. What offer does the narrator make in the last lines of the poem?

Thinking About the Poem

11. Using images to reveal emotion, write a brief letter from the husband to the wife telling her that he has received her letter and that he will be coming down through the narrows.

Name Class Date

Patterns

by Amy Lowell

Read the short biography of Lowell on page 496. Then read the entire poem, which is set in the late 1700s in Europe. Note that a squill is a kind of flower. Answer the questions below.

1. Where is the poem's narrator in the first stanza?

2. How does the poem's narrator describe herself?

3. List the patterns that the poet mentions in the first stanza.

4. Even though she doesn't use conventional rhyme schemes in this poem, Lowell does make use of rhyme. Find all the examples of rhyme that you can in this first stanza.

5. What contrast does the poet begin to develop in the first stanza?

6. What imagery does the poet use in the second stanza to continue to develop the contrast she has set up?

7. What would the woman like to do with her gown? Why?

8. What does the woman imagine doing in lines 43-50?

9. What is the news in the letter the woman has received?

10. What do you think the blossom that falls on the woman's bosom symbolizes?

11. What plans did the two lovers make? What special poignancy does the lime tree have for the woman? (lines 81-90)

12. What future does the woman envision for herself?

Name Class Date

Chicago

by Carl Sandburg

Read the short biography of Sandburg on page 496. Then read the entire poem. Answer the questions below.

1. What are the industries that the city of Chicago is known for, according to the poem?

2. Below are three of the characteristics that critics of the city attribute to Chicago. Fill in the blanks with the evidence the speaker cites to support these criticisms.

wicked: ______

crooked: ______

brutal: ______

3. What does the speaker give back to the people who sneer at Chicago? Why?

4. What image does Sandburg present in line 11 to contrast Chicago with "little soft cities"?

5. List the words or phrases in line 11 that the poet uses to evoke a sense of intense activity?

6. In line 12, what are the two similes Sandburg uses to describe the city?

7. What effect does the poet achieve in lines 13-17?

8. What kind of laughter is described in the poem's last lines?

9. What are the specific attributes of this laughter?

10. How does the poem come full circle?

Name Class Date

Poetry
by Marianne Moore

Read the short biography on page 497. Then read the entire poem, which serves as the poet's explanation of what makes for genuine poetry.

1. In the poem's first line, what does the speaker admit to disliking?

2. What reason does the speaker give for disliking "it"?

3. What meaning of the word *fiddle* do you think the speaker has in mind?

4. What does the speaker discover in poetry, despite her feelings about it?

5. List the concrete details Moore uses in the first stanza to illustrate the effect that the "genuine" can have.

6. What do we all have in common, according to the speaker?

7. What are some of the things that we "cannot understand"?

8. What do all the phenomena listed in the poem have in common?

9. What prevents these phenomena from being poetry, according to the speaker?

10. What does the speaker believe poets have to be in order to make poetry?

11. What qualities do poets have to rise above in order to create poetry?

12. What phrase does the poet use to represent what poetry should be?

13. What two demands indicate an interest in poetry, according to the poem?

Thinking About the Poem

14. Look at the list of things in lines 11-15 that the poem indicates we "cannot understand." On another sheet of paper, discuss what it is about them that we have trouble understanding.

Name _______________ Class _______ Date _______

Spring and All
by William Carlos Williams

Read the short biography of Williams on page 497. Then read the entire poem.

1. Where does the poem open?

2. What word does Williams use to describe the hospital?

3. What time of year is it? What imagery does the poet use in the first six lines to evoke the time of year?

4. What quality of the weeds does Williams emphasize?

5. Make a list of the words the poet uses in lines 5-13 to evoke the cold, dormant quality of the season.

6. In lines 14 and 15, the poet describes three aspects of approaching spring. What are they?

7. What do you think the poet has in mind using the above words to describe spring?

8. What is it that the new life entering the world knows for certain?

9. What is the environment like to the new life that enters the world?

10. Besides the new grass and the carrot leaf, what other kinds of new life do you think the poet might have in mind in this poem?

11. What phrase does the poet use to mark the beginning of life?

12. What do you think the poet has in mind with the phrase "the profound change"?

Name Class Date

Ars Poetica

by Archibald MacLeish

Read the short biography of MacLeish on page 497. Then read the entire poem, in which MacLeish defines what poetry is and does.

1. What are the two qualities of "globed fruit" that the speaker compares to the qualities a poem should have?

2. Look up the words *palpable* and *mute* if you don't know what they mean. Rewrite the first two lines of the poem using the definitions of these two words instead of the words themselves.

3. What quality should a poem have as indicated in lines 3 and 4?

4. What quality should a poem have as indicated in lines 5 and 6?

5. What quality should a poem have as indicated in lines 7 and 8?

6. In what way do you think an old medallion would be dumb "to the thumb"?

7. What do you think the poet has in mind when he says that a poem should be "wordless as a flight of birds"?

8. What is another quality a poem should have as indicated in lines 9 and 10?

9. What images does the poet use to represent grief?

10. What images does the poet use to represent love?

11. What quality of poetry is described in the last two lines?

Thinking About the Poem

12. Do you think MacLeish would have much faith in the kinds of questions you are answering on this page about his poem? Explain.

Name Class Date

Birches, Fire and Ice, "Out, Out—", Stopping by Woods on a Snowy Evening, and Mending Wall

by Robert Frost

Birches

Read the biography on page 509. Then read the entire poem. Answer the five questions below.

1. What is the subject of the poem?

2. What bends birches down to stay?

3. Make a list of the specifics that the poet gives about the imagined boy and his life.

4. How does this imagined boy resemble the speaker of the poem?

5. What wish does the speaker have? How does he fear that it might be misunderstood?

Fire and Ice

1. Read the entire poem. What are two ways the world might end, according to this poem?

2. Which side of the fire-versus-ice argument does the speaker come out on? Why?

3. The speaker makes an argument for the belief that the world will end in ice. What is that argument?

4. Fire and ice each symbolize an emotion in the poem. Name them.

5. List other emotions you could connect to the words *fire* and *ice*.

   fire:

   ice:

"Out, Out—"

1. Read the entire poem. What is the setting in the first eight lines of the poem? Give details.

Name ______ Class ______ Date ______

2. What language does the poet use to personify the saw?

3. What request does the boy make of his sister?

4. What is the response of the people in the poem to the boy's death? What do you think the poet wants to say about death?

Stopping by Woods on a Snowy Evening

1. Where is the poem's speaker, and what are the circumstances of the poem?

2. What does the speaker's horse find odd, according to the speaker?

3. Fill in the blanks below with an example of each of the following sound devices used in the poem.

   rhyme: ______

   alliteration: ______

   assonance: ______

   consonance: ______

4. What quality of sound does the poet evoke in stanza 3?

Mending Wall

1. Read the entire poem. What are some of the ways that walls are sabotaged, according to the poem?

2. What is mysterious about the gaps that appear in walls?

3. What does the speaker compare repairing the wall to?

4. Why does the poem's speaker think that a wall is not necessary?

5. What maxim does the speaker's neighbor use in defense of keeping a wall between them?

6. What questions would the speaker ask before building a wall?

Name Class Date

Theme for English B
by Langston Hughes

Read the short biography of Hughes on page 516. Read the entire poem, then answer the questions.

1. What circumstance prompted the speaker to write this poem?

2. List a few facts about himself that the speaker gives in lines 6-15.

3. List some of the things the speaker likes.

4. What does the speaker have to say about the effect being black has on his likes and dislikes?

5. In what way do the speaker and instructor, though different, affect each other?

6. Follow the instructor's directions given at the beginning of the poem and write your own brief poem, letting it "come out of you."

November Cotton Flower
by Jean Toomer

Read the short biography of Toomer page 516. Then read the entire poem and answer the questions.

1. What do the cotton stalks look like?

2. What has made the cotton stalks look the way they do?

3. What does the poet compare the scarcity of cotton to?

4. What other conditions of hardship prevail on the land?

5. What miraculous event occurs in the midst of all this hardship?

6. What effect does this event have on the people?

Name Class Date

Any Human to Another
by Countee Cullen

Read the short biography of Cullen on page 516, then read the entire poem. Answer the questions below.

1. Rewrite the anastrophe in the first six lines so that the sentence is no longer inverted.

2. In what way are people connected to each other, according to the speaker?

3. What caution does the speaker issue in lines 13-19?

4. How do joy and sorrow differ, according to the poem?

5. What similes does Cullen use to describe the effect a person's grief and sorrow has on others?

   grief:

   sorrow:

The Creation
by James Weldon Johnson

Read the short biography of Johnson on page 517. Then read the poem and answer the questions below.

1. What reason does the poet give for God's making himself a world?

2. What image does the poet use to describe the darkness that covered everything?

3. Fill in the blanks below with the method that God uses to make the items listed.

   sun:

   moon and stars:

   valleys and mountains:

   seven seas:

4. When God says, "Bring forth! Bring forth!" what creatures come forth?

5. Even though he has created a world full of wonder, how does God feel?

6. How does God create man? What simile does Johnson use to describe it? Answer these questions on a separate piece of paper.

Name Class Date

A Black Man Talks of Reaping
by Arna Bontemps

Read the short biography on page 517, then read the entire poem. Answer the seven questions below.

1. What does the phrase "beside all waters" suggest?

2. What fear has the narrator of the poem felt?

3. What event does the narrator anticipate and plan for?

4. What does the narrator have to show for all the seed that he has sown?

5. Find an example of alliteration in the second stanza.

6. What are the "brother's sons" reaping?

7. The word *glean* means to pick the fields clean of what has been left by reapers. What, then, do the narrator's own children get of what he has planted?

If We Must Die
by Claude McKay

Read the biography on page 517. McKay wrote this poem in response to urban race riots of 1919. Read the poem, answering all questions.

1. What does the poet's choice of imagery—"hogs hunted and penned"—symbolize?

2. Who do the "mad and hungry dogs" represent?

3. What must the speaker and his people do in order to force the "monsters" to honor them, even though they may honor the dead?

4. Find an example of apostrophe in this poem.

5. Even though outnumbered, how does the speaker exhort his people to find courage to fight?

6. The word *pack* expands on which image? Why is it an effective word?

Name Class Date

The Love Song of J. Alfred Prufrock

by T. S. Eliot

Read the biography on page 525. This poem is a dramatic monologue in which the speaker, Prufrock, talks to himself about the state of his life. Read the entire poem, then answer the questions below.

1. What simile does the poet use to describe the evening sky?

2. What is the mood of the first stanza? List the words Eliot uses to establish this mood.

3. The women bustle and chit-chat about one of the finest artists who ever lived. Do you think they really care about the work of Michelangelo? Explain.

4. What is the central image of the section that begins on line 15? What animal does it seem to represent?

5. What does the animal do?

6. List three of the things there will be time for as indicated in lines 23-36.

7. What do you think these lines say about Prufrock's nature?

8. In lines 37-48, the speaker presents a picture of his physical self. How would you describe him, based on the information in this section?

9. Eliot uses sound devices to create a musical effect. Below, list examples of these devices found in lines 37-48.

   rhyme: ________

   consonance: ________

   alliteration: ________

10. What do you think Prufrock is saying about himself when he says, "I have measured out my life in coffee spoons"?

11. What do the eyes in lines 55-61 do?

12. Briefly describe the arms in lines 62-69.

Name Class Date

13. What does Prufrock say he should have been? What do you think he means by this image?

14. What previous imagery does the image of the evening (lines 75-78) sleeping peacefully "stretched on the floor" recall?

15. What do you think the "crisis" is that the speaker both anticipates and wishes to avoid?

16. What emotion does the speaker end this section of the poem with?

17. How does the speaker rationalize his failure to force a crisis in the section beginning on line 87?

18. What powerful image does the poet then use to present Prufrock's overwhelming feelings about the question he might have asked?

19. The poet shifts from the abstract to the specific in lines 99-110. List the concrete, everyday items he names in this section.

20. What literary allusion occurs in line 111?

21. How does the speaker describe himself and his place in the drama of his life?

22. From line 120 on, the tone shifts. What new tone do you detect in the narrative voice?

23. What do you think the speaker's lament "I grow old . . . I grow old" signifies about his state of mind?

Thinking About the Poem

24. Think about the image of the mermaids with which Eliot closes the poem. How does this image contrast with imagery found throughout the poem? Why do you think the poet concludes the poem with this image? Write your answers on another sheet of paper.

Name Class Date

Abraham Lincoln Walks at Midnight
by Vachel Lindsay

Read the short biography of Lindsay on page 532, then read the entire poem. Answer the questions below.

1. What occurrence takes place at midnight in the small town of Springfield, Illinois?

2. In what places does this restless figure choose to walk?

3. The poet uses several familiar images to clue the reader in to the identity of the mysterious, pacing figure. What are these images?

4. What issue is of such deep concern to Lincoln?

5. When will he be able to rest again?

6. What does Lindsay say is breaking Lincoln's heart?

7. What question does the poet pose in the last stanza of the poem?

The Mountain Woman
by DuBose Heyward

Read the short biography of Heyward on page 532, then read the entire poem. Answer the questions below.

1. What mood does the poet create in the first stanza? What language does he use to accomplish this?

2. What is the woman's lot in life? How is she affected by it?

3. What tragedy occurs in the third stanza?

4. How does the mountain woman handle this tragedy?

5. What does her husband do that proves to be the last straw?

6. Why do you think the woman cried at this action and not at the death of her son?

Name ______ Class ______ Date ______

Well, I Have Lost You

by Edna St. Vincent Millay

Read the short biography of Millay on page 532, then read the entire poem. Answer the six questions below.

1. What has happened to the speaker in the first two lines of the poem?

2. Who does the speaker blame for her situation, if anyone?

3. What source of pride do you think the speaker can find in her situation?

4. What metaphor does the poet use to describe why she accepted the situation rather than fight against it?

5. How does the speaker console herself for her loss?

6. How does the speaker anticipate feeling in the future?

Pretty Words

by Elinor Wylie

Read the short biography of Wylie on page 533, then read the entire poem. Answer all the questions.

1. What metaphor does the poet use to describe the words that poets use?

2. Below is a list of words that Wylie uses in describing the kinds of words she loves. Next to each word, fill in the blank with the simile or metaphor the poet uses.

   smooth: ______

   tender: ______

   shy: ______

3. What metaphor does the poet introduce in lines 9 and 10 to capture the qualities of words that she loves?

4. What unexpected note does the poem end on?

5. Think of your own metaphor for language. On a separate sheet of paper make a list of the things you love about words.

Name Class Date

Boats in a Fog

by Robinson Jeffers

Read the short biography on page 533, then read the entire poem. Answer the questions below.

1. List the diversions the poet says appeal to children, but which "lack nobility."

2. What quality does the poet look for in beauty?

3. What is the sudden shift that takes place in line 6 of the poem?

4. What circumstance does the poet describe in the poem?

5. What mood is established by the poet in this description? Select words from the poem to support your answer.

6. How are boats returning to harbor like the flight of pelicans or of planets?

The Solitary

by Sara Teasdale

Read the short biography on page 533. Then read the entire poem and answer the five questions below.

1. What has the "passing of the years" brought to the speaker?

2. What things does the speaker treasure about her life now?

3. What do you think the tone of the last stanza is? What do you learn about the speaker from it?

4. Do you think the speaker cares about others? Support your answer from the text.

5. Think about the phrase "self-complete as a flower or a stone." What do you think it means? Do you feel that way?

Name Class Date

Anecdote of the Jar
by Wallace Stevens

Read the short biography of Stevens on page 540, then read the poem. Answer the questions below.

1. What is the main action in the poem?

2. What effect does the jar have on the wilderness?

3. Look up the word *slovenly* if you don't know what it means. What does the word's connotation imply about the wilderness?

4. What do you think the jar might be a symbol of?

5. What do you think the poet's point of view about nature is?

Janet Waking
by John Crowe Ransom

Read the short biography on page 540, then read the entire poem. Answer the six questions below.

1. What is Janet doing when the poem opens?

2. What is her first thought of the day?

3. How has Janet's world changed overnight?

4. Look up the word *transmogrifying* if you don't know what it means. What does the poet have in mind when he describes the bee as transmogrifying?

5. Janet cannot understand the deep "forgetful kingdom of sleep." What is the kingdom of sleep, and in what way is it forgetful?

6. What do you think the poet's tone is in contemplating Janet's first encounter with death?

Name Class Date

anyone lived in a pretty how town and 1 (a

by E. E. Cummings

anyone lived in a pretty how town

Read the short biography on page 540 and the Reader's Note on page 543. Now read the entire poem, whose two main characters are anyone and noone. Answer the eight questions below.

1. Below is a list of words that appear in the first stanza. Fill in the blanks with their opposites, which also appear in the stanza.

   up: ______ summer: ______

   did: ______

2. In stanza 2, who do the men and women in the town dislike? What do they sow and reap?

3. In stanzas 3 and 4, who do we learn noone loves?

4. List the verbs that appear in stanza 5. Who are the people that seem to perform these actions?

5. What effect does the phrase "stars rain sun moon" achieve in stanza 6?

6. What happens to anyone and noone in stanza 7?

7. Find a paradox in the last stanza of the poem.

8. What do you think the poem is all about?

1(a

Read the entire poem. Read the second part of the Reader's Note, on page 544, for help in understanding this poem.

1. Write the words of the poem out in sentence form. What are the words that fall within the parentheses?

2. What is the word outside of the parentheses?

3. What connection can you draw between the words inside and outside of the parentheses?

4. What does the poem's content suggest to you about its structure?

5. Look up the word *solitude*. On a separate sheet of paper write your own poem about solitude, using no more than five words.

Name Class Date

Lament of the Normal Child

by Phyllis McGinley

Read the short biography of McGinley on page 541. Then read the entire poem, answering the questions below.

1. What rule does the narrator's school follow?

2. What difference exists between the speaker and the rest of the children in school?

3. What phrase does the speaker of the poem use to describe his normalcy in stanza 2?

4. In the list below, fill in the blanks with each child's appropriate "fixation."

   Frederick Knipe:

   Cuthbert Jones:

   Jessamine Gray:

   Mortimer Sears:

5. What is the narrator's lament, exactly?

Childhood

by Margaret Walker

Read the short biography on page 541, then read the entire poem. Answer all the questions.

1. Briefly describe the miners that the narrator knew as a child.

2. What meanings of the word *undermining* do you think can be applied to the poem?

3. What events colored the poet's "low cotton country" childhood?

4. What emotion holds sway over the land?

5. The poet writes "only bitter *land* was washed away." What remained behind?

Name Class Date

University Days

by James Thurber

Beginning the Story

Read the biography on page 548, then read the story to page 550, column 2, where Professor Bassum says, "Quite right, . . ."

1. What reason does the narrator give for failing botany?

2. What does he see when he looks through his microscope?

3. What is the botany instructor's response to the narrator's difficulties?

4. The narrator is finally able to draw something he sees through the microscope. What is it?

5. Who is the mixed-up student in economics class? What is his real talent?

6. Find an example of irony in the narrator's description of Bolenciecwcz's intelligence.

7. What is the question the professor asks Bolenciecwcz? What do the class and the instructor do to help Bolenciecwcz figure out the answer?

Continuing the Story

Read the story to the end, answering the questions.

8. What help did the narrator get in passing his swimming test?

9. Who is Haskins? Why did he decide to take up journalism?

10. What hot news does Haskins finally dig up about the horses?

11. What irony of situation does the narrator describe about the military drill that each student had to take?

12. Briefly describe the narrator's one triumph during military drill.

Thinking About the Story

13. On a separate sheet of paper, discuss one of the situations in the story that made you laugh. If nothing made you laugh, explain why.

Name Class Date

from **One Writer's Beginnings**

by Eudora Welty

Beginning the Selection

Read the selection to page 554, column 2, through the paragraph that begins "The journey took about a week each way, ..."

1. What role does the narrator's mother play in the family's travels?

2. How does the narrator's mother view the road?

3. Briefly describe the conditions under which the family traveled.

4. What effect did the long journey—the road—have on the narrator's father?

5. In what characteristic does the narrator resemble her father?

Continuing the Selection

Read until you finish the selection, answering the questions below.

6. What simile does the narrator use to describe the rope used by the ferryman?

7. How does the narrator characterize her mother's and her father's temperaments? How do they differ from each other?

8. What event does the narrator write about as an illustration of her mother's willingness to take risks?

9. What does the narrator's mother remain afraid of?

10. In what ways are towns like people, according to the narrator?

Thinking About the Selection

11. The narrator uses the phrase "going 'through the country' " at the beginning and end of the selection. On a separate sheet of paper, discuss the shifts in meaning you find in the way the phrase is used.

Name ________ Class ________ Date ________

Tell Your Children

by The Grand Council Fire of American Indians

Read the entire selection, answering the questions below.

1. When white people use the phrase "America First," what do the speakers in this selection want them to remember and to tell their children?

2. In what ways do school histories use language to distort history in unjust ways, according to the speakers?

3. What two battles do the speakers use to support their contention?

4. What argument do the speakers make to explain why Indians fought white people?

5. Once again, the speakers point out that language is used to perpetuate unjust perceptions of Indians. What language is used unjustly?

6. When white people call Indians treacherous, which of their own actions are they overlooking?

7. Listed below are two words used by white people to describe Indians. Use the blanks provided to fill in the counter-argument presented by the speakers.

   thieves: ________

   savages: ________

8. What sounds can be heard in the melodies of Indian songs?

9. List some of the things that the speakers want white people to teach their children about Indian culture and history.

10. What points are made about Indians who fought in World War I?

Name Class Date

The Glass Menagerie: Act One, Scenes 1, 2, and 3

by Tennessee Williams

Beginning Act One: Scene 1

Read the biography on page 570, and the Comment on page 580. Then read the selection to the end of Act One, Scene 1. Answer the questions below as you read.

1. Read the stage directions for Scene 1. What information does the playwright give about the dual function of the character Tom?

2. Read Tom's opening speech. What characteristics does the narrator use to describe the term *memory play?*

3. What does Tom tell us about his father?

4. What is Tom's response to his mother's instructions on how to eat properly?

5. What characteristics did all of Amanda's gentlemen callers have in common?

6. What is Amanda's fear about her daughter's future, according to Laura?

Continuing Act One: Scene 2

Continue reading the play to the end of Scene 2. Answer the questions.

7. What is Laura doing before her mother comes in at the beginning of the scene? What does she do when she hears her mother coming?

8. When Laura asks her mother if she went to the D.A.R. meeting, what is Amanda's response? What does she do?

9. What has Amanda discovered that makes her so upset with Laura?

10. What explanation does Laura give for not attending Rubicam's Business College?

Name ______ Class ______ Date ______

11. What picture does Amanda paint of the life Laura faces as a dependent, if she cannot support herself?

______

______

12. Briefly describe Jim, the boy Laura liked in high school.

______

______

13. What is Laura's response when her mother indicates that she will see to it that Laura ends up with a nice young man?

______

14. What does Amanda tell Laura she must do to counteract her "slight defect"?

______

Continuing Act One: Scene 3

Continue reading the play through to the end of Scene 3, answering the questions below.

15. What is Tom's role in his speech at the start of Scene 3?

______

16. What idea takes over all of Amanda Wingfield's energies after the Rubicam's Business College incident?

______

______

17. How does the quarrel between Tom and his mother begin?

______

______

18. What does Tom accuse Amanda of doing? What accusation does Amanda make to Tom about his activities?

______

______

______

19. Tom reacts to his mother's refusal to believe he is going to the movies by detailing a number of disreputable activities he claims to be involved in. Check the one activity below Tom *does not* name.

_____ carries a tommy gun in a violin case	_____ joined the Hogan gang
_____ goes to gambling casinos	_____ goes to opium dens
_____ drives the get-away car for a gang of bank robbers	_____ is a czar of the underworld
	_____ wears a patch and false mustache

20. What happens when Tom throws his coat across the room?

______

Thinking About Scenes 1, 2, and 3

21. How would you describe the tone of Tom's parting speech?

______

Name Class Date

The Glass Menagerie: Act One, Scenes 4, 5, and 6

by Tennessee Williams

Continuing Act One: Scene 4

Continue reading the play to the end of Scene 4. Answer the questions below as you read.

1. What is Tom's condition when he returns to the apartment later that night?

2. Who is Malvolio? List some of the things he does.

3. Where previously in the play does Tom talk about magician's tricks?

Continuing Act One: Scene 5

Continue reading the play through to the end of Scene 5, answering the questions below as you read.

4. What plea does Laura make to Tom at the beginning of Scene 5?

5. What is the mood between Tom and Amanda at the start of this scene?

6. What promise does Amanda ask Tom to make?

7. What reason does Tom give for going to the movies so much?

8. Amanda tells Tom that Laura was crying. What was the reason, according to Amanda?

9. According to Tom, what is man, by instinct?

10. What is Amanda's view of instinct?

11. What does Amanda tell Tom will have to happen before he can join the Merchant Marine?

12. What does Amanda ask Tom to do at the warehouse? What is Tom's reply?

Name Class Date

Continuing Act One: Scene 6

Continue reading the play through to the end of Scene 6. Answer the questions below.

13. How would you describe Tom's first speech in Scene 6?

14. What good news does Tom have for Amanda at the beginning of this scene?

15. How does Amanda react to the news that the visitor is coming the next evening?

16. Why does Amanda decide to make salmon loaf with mayonnaise for the caller?

17. What does O'Connor do at the warehouse, and what does Tom judge he earns?

18. How did Amanda make the "tragic mistake" that she did in choosing her husband?

19. What does James D. O'Connor look like, according to Tom?

20. What makes Tom think that O'Connor is "up and coming"?

21. What kind of picture of Laura does Tom create as he speaks to his mother?

Thinking About Scenes 4, 5, and 6

22. On a separate sheet of paper, compare and contrast Amanda and Laura. In what ways are they alike? In what ways are they different?

Name Class Date

The Glass Menagerie: Act Two, Scenes 7 and 8

by Tennessee Williams

Beginning Act Two: Scene 7

Read this scene from beginning to end to learn more about the much-anticipated Mr. O'Connor. Answer the questions below as you read.

1. How does Jim O'Connor's life after high school differ from his high school years, according to Tom?

2. What state of mind is Laura in when Scene 7 opens? What has caused her mood?

3. What is Amanda's response when Laura says, "You make it seem like we were setting a trap"?

4. What story does Amanda tell about jonquils? What does the story tell you about Amanda's personality?

5. What worries Laura when she hears the name of the "gentleman caller"?

6. How does Laura behave as she first sees Jim?

7. When Jim tells Tom that he is going to be out of a job if he doesn't "wake up," what does Tom say?

8. Why, according to Tom, do people go to the movies? When do people "come out of the dark room"?

9. How did Tom pay his union dues?

10. In what way does Tom seem like his father in his talk with Jim?

11. What kind of impression does Amanda make on Jim O'Connor?

12. How would you describe the change that comes over Amanda in this scene?

Name Class Date

13. How does Amanda describe her past to Jim O'Connor?

Continuing Act Two: Scene 8

Read the Reader's Note on page 597 before continuing the play. Then continue reading to the end of the play. Answer the questions below as you read.

14. What event starts off the beginning of Scene 8?

15. What does Amanda say Jim can do to "help" while she and Tom are washing the dishes?

16. What does Jim O'Connor do to make Laura comfortable as they sit in the front room?

17. How do Laura's memories of her late entrances to chorus differ from Jim O'Connor's?

18. What reason does Laura give Jim for having been so shy?

19. What is Jim O'Connor's main disappointment in life?

20. What does Jim judge Laura's problem to be?

21. What does Laura indicate to Jim she is more interested in than anything else?

22. How does Laura react to the discovery that the unicorn has lost its horn?

23. Why can't Jim O'Connor take Laura out on the date that he feels she deserves?

24. When Amanda accuses Tom of playing a joke on them by bringing home a "gentleman caller" already engaged to be married, what does Tom do?

Thinking About the Play

25. On a separate sheet of paper, discuss what you think Laura's glass unicorn may be a symbol of.

Name Class Date

Man and Daughter in the Cold

by John Updike

Beginning the Story

Read the biography on page 632. Then read the story through to the end of the conversation in the gondola between Becky and Ethan, on page 634, column 2.

1. Who are the characters introduced in the first paragraph of this story?

2. Find and list as many descriptions of the weather in the first paragraph as you can.

3. What does Ethan find strange in Becky's behavior when she joins him and Matt at the bottom of the hill?

4. What is Matt Langley's opinion of Becky's skiing?

5. What sensations aggravate Ethan's asthma attacks?

Continuing the Story

Continue reading the story to the end, answering the questions.

6. What is Ethan's reaction to youth after fifteen years of teaching?

7. Find similes and other figures of speech in the next few paragraphs that describe the cold and its effect on Ethan.

8. What happens to Ethan during the run down the mountainside? How does Becky help her father?

9. What does Becky tell her father about his asthma? What is Ethan's response to Becky's "lecture"?

Thinking About the Story

10. In the last line of the story, Ethan glimpses in Becky "something generic and joyous, a pageant that would leave him behind." Where else in the story is this sense of being left behind developed? Answer the question on a separate sheet of paper.

Name ____________________ Class ____________ Date ____________

The First Seven Years

by Bernard Malamud

Beginning the Story

Read the biography on page 640. Then read the selection to page 644, column 1, through the paragraph that begins "After the incident with the broken last . . . the shoemaker decided to let him stew. . . ."

1. Briefly describe the feelings Feld has for Max, the college boy, and for Miriam, his daughter.

2. What is Sobel's relationship with Feld and with Miriam?

3. What plan does Feld decide to put into action when Max shows up at the shop needing repairs on his shoes?

4. Briefly describe Max's appearance.

5. What action of Sobel's causes Feld great anxiety? Why does Sobel's action worry Feld?

Continuing the Story

Read the story to the end, answering the questions below.

6. How did Miriam like her first date with Max? Support your answer.

7. Why does Miriam decide, after their second date, that she doesn't like Max?

8. After his heart attack, Feld goes to ask Sobel to come back to work for him. Why is Sobel angry with Feld?

9. What condition does Feld make for Sobel to ask to marry Miriam?

Thinking About the Story

10. What do you think will happen when Sobel does propose to Miriam? Answer the question on a separate sheet of paper.

Name Class Date

The Wooing of Ariadne

by Harry Mark Petrakis

Beginning the Story

Read the biography on page 649. Then read the selection through to the break on page 654, column 2.

1. From what point of view is the story written?

2. What is Marko Palamas's view of women? Use the text to support your answer.

3. Briefly describe Ariadne Langos's responses to Marko Palamas's advances during their first meeting.

4. How does Marko manage to find encouragement to pursue Ariadne despite her unconditional rejection of him?

5. Briefly describe Marko Palamas's second meeting with Ariadne.

Continuing the Story

Continue reading the story through to the end.

6. Who is at the church when Marko and Ariadne's father arrive?

7. How would you describe the mood in the church during this meeting?

8. What are the concerns of Ariadne's family voiced by Father Marlas?

9. How does Marko Palamas explain his behavior towards Ariadne?

Thinking About the Story

10. Why do you think Ariadne changed her mind about Marko Palamas? Write your answer on another sheet of paper.

Name Class Date

The Haunted Boy

by Carson Smith McCullers

Beginning the Story

Read the biography on page 659. Then read the selection to the line where John says, "I hate to eat and run . . ." (page 662, column 2).

1. What makes Hugh think something is wrong when he comes home from school? What does he remember?

2. What does Hugh admire about his friend John?

3. What is Hugh most worried about?

4. What does John's use of Hugh's first name signify to Hugh the first time he hears it?

5. What does it signify to Hugh the next time John calls him "Hugh"?

6. What happened to Hugh's mother that causes Hugh and his father such concern?

Continuing the Story

Read the story through to the end. Answer the questions below.

7. What does Hugh do to keep John from leaving?

8. What makes Hugh start to cry? Why does he cry so hard?

9. Why is Hugh so angry at his mother?

10. What praise does Hugh's father bestow on him? How does the praise affect Hugh?

Thinking About the Story

11. The title of the story describes Hugh as being a "haunted" boy. In what ways do you think the word *haunted* might also apply to Hugh's mother? Write your answer on a separate piece of paper.

Name Class Date

Harrison Bergeron

by Kurt Vonnegut, Jr.

Beginning the Story

Read the biography on page 668. Then read the selection to page 670, column 2, through the paragraph that begins "He finally gave up, handed the bulletin to a ballerina to read."

1. What condition of life in the year 2081 is important to this story?

2. What happens in April in the year 2081?

3. How are George and Hazel prevented from thinking about their son's disappearance?

4. How are the ballerinas made to be "no better than anybody else"?

5. What prevents George from thinking about his "abnormal son," Harrison, who has gone to jail?

6. For which crime could George Bergeron receive two years in prison and two thousand dollars in fines?

Continuing the Story

Read the story to the end, answering the questions below.

7. Why is Harrison considered dangerous, according to the news?

8. Below is a list of events. Number them in the order they occur.

____ Diana Moon Glampers, Handicapper General, invades the studio with a shotgun.

____ Harrison Bergeron declares that he is the Emperor.

____ Harrison Bergeron strips off his physical and mental handicaps.

____ Harrison Bergeron dances with the ballerina.

____ Harrison Bergeron's picture appears on the television screen.

9. How do Hazel and George Bergeron respond to these events?

Thinking About the Story

10. Vonnegut is satirizing certain aspects of American society in this story. On a separate piece of paper, discuss the object of his satire.

Name Class Date

The Life You Save May Be Your Own

by Flannery O'Connor

Beginning the Story

Read the biography on page 674. Then read the selection to the space on page 677, column 2.

1. In the space below, briefly describe the story's main characters.

   Tom T. Shiftlet: ______

   Lucynell Crater (mother): ______

   Lucynell Crater (daughter): ______

2. What offer does the old woman make to Tom Shiftlet?

3. How does the author describe the moon?

4. What do you think Tom Shiftlet and the mother want from each other?

Continuing the Story

Read to the end of the story, answering the questions below.

5. What word does the old woman want Shiftlet to teach her daughter next?

6. How old is the girl?

7. How does the old woman finally ask Tom to marry her daughter?

8. Why isn't Tom Shiftlet satisfied with the marriage proceedings?

9. What is Tom Shiflet's mood when he looks at Lucynell beside him?

10. What does the hitchhiker say that shocks Tom Shiftlet?

Thinking About the Story

11. On a separate piece of paper, tell why you think Tom Shiftlet leaves Lucynell at The Hot Spot.

Name Class Date

Marigolds

by Eugenia Collier

Beginning the Story

Read the biography on page 683. Then read the story to page 686, column 2, through the paragraph that begins "Miss Lottie's marigolds were perhaps the strangest part of the picture."

1. What is the first thing the narrator remembers about her home town?

2. What emotions do the narrator's memories of the marigolds evoke?

3. What distinguishes Miss Lottie's house from the rest of the houses in the neighborhood?

4. How do the children of the neighborhood see Miss Lottie?

Continuing the Story

Continue reading the story to the end, answering the questions.

5. According to the narrator, why do the children hate the marigolds so much?

6. How does the narrator feel about having led the taunting and harassment of Miss Lottie?

7. What frightens the narrator about the conversation she overhears between her parents that night?

8. What are all the feelings that flood the narrator and "combine in one great impulse toward destruction"?

Thinking About the Story

9. When her "last act of childhood" is done with, what reality about Miss Lottie does the narrator finally see? Why do you think this insight marks the end of the narrator's childhood? Discuss these questions on a separate sheet of paper.

Name Class Date

The Secret

by Denise Levertov

Read the short biography of Levertov on page 692, then read the entire poem.

1. What situation does the poem's first stanza describe? Rephrase it in your own words.

2. What information about the secret does the poet lack? (lines 5-13)

3. What does the poet assume about the girls and the secret a week later?

4. What will the two girls discover over and over, and where?

5. What does the poet love in the two girls most of all?

The Writer

by Richard Wilbur

Read the biography of Wilbur on page 692, then read the entire poem.

1. What is the narrator's daughter doing?

2. What simile does the narrator use to describe the effect of the "commotion" of typewriter keys?

3. What metaphor does the narrator use to describe his daughter's life? Explain.

4. What memory comes to the narrator's mind?

5. What language does the poet use to describe the starling's desperation?

6. What connection does the narrator make between his daughter and the starling?

Name Class Date

To David, About His Education
by Howard Nemerov

Read Nemerov's short biography on page 692, then read the entire poem. Answer the questions below.

1. Who is the poem addressed to, and what is it about?

2. How will David have to learn the "mostly invisible things" of the world, according to the speaker?

3. List the "things" David must learn. What do they have in common?

4. What do you think the speaker's tone is when his describes the things David will learn?

5. What do adults—and education in general—really teach children to do, according to the poem?

The Vision Test
by Mona Van Duyn

Read the short biography of Mona Van Duyn on page 692, then read the entire poem.

1. What do the title and the first two lines of the poem tell you about the subject and setting of the poem?

2. What does the speaker think of the woman administering the vision test?

3. What profession does the speaker give in answer to the woman's question?

4. How does the woman in charge respond to the speaker's information?

5. What does the woman's next question tell you about her opinion of the speaker?

Name Class Date

Frederick Douglass
by Robert Hayden

Read the short biography on page 698, then read the entire poem.

1. Who is the poem about?

2. What necessary and usable elements does the poet compare freedom to?

3. When freedom "belongs to all," what characteristic will it exhibit?

4. Look up the words *diastole* and *systole* if you don't know what they mean. Why do you think the poet chose these two words?

5. What kind of world did Frederick Douglass envision, according to the poet?

6. What will be the truest testimony to Frederick Douglass's vision?

My Father's Garden
by David Wagoner

Read the biography of Wagoner on page 698, then read the poem.

1. The temperature in the first stanza of the poem is hot. What language does the poet use to create this atmosphere of heat?

2. What is the father's garden, actually?

3. In stanza 2, the poet uses language describing two worlds, the garden and the scrapyard. Fill in the lists below with the language appropriate to each.

Garden	Scrapyard

4. What did the speaker's father try to do? Was he successful?

5. What did the father retain of his education? What use did he put this to?

Name ______ Class ______ Date ______

Judgments
by William Stafford

Read the short biography on page 698, then read the entire poem.

1. Fill in the blanks below with the accusations the speaker makes against each of the people listed. Use your own words.

Ellen	George	Tom
______	______	______
______	______	______
______	______	______

2. What memory of himself and these people does the speaker have?

______

______

3. What thing does the speaker see that hasn't changed at all?

______

4. What does the speaker accuse himself of?

______

______

5. What do you think is the one thing the speaker is most concerned with when making his accusations against himself and his friends?

______

______

Mr. Edwards and the Spider
by Robert Lowell

Read the biography on page 698 and the Reader's Note on page 703, which gives important background. Then read the entire poem and answer the questions.

1. In stanza 1, what does the speaker of the poem see in August?

______

2. What happens to the spiders in November?

______

3. In stanza 2, what do the phrases "treason crackling in your blood" and "sickness past your cure" refer to?

______

4. What power do the worm and the spider hold, in stanza 4?

______

5. How does the speaker describe death in stanzas 4 and 5?

______

______

Name Class Date

The Groundhog

by Richard Eberhart

Read the short biography on page 705 and the Reader's Note on page 707. Then read the entire poem.

1. What is the setting of the poem, as established in the first few lines?

2. Briefly describe in your own words the narrator's response in lines 5-24 to seeing the dead groundhog being devoured by maggots.

3. What changes have both the narrator and the groundhog undergone by the time the narrator returns in the autumn? (lines 25-32)

4. What does the narrator find when he next chances on the groundhog? (lines 33-40)

5. What parallel do you think the narrator draws between the groundhog and China, Greece, Alexander, Montaigne, and Saint Teresa?

Snow by Morning

by May Swenson

Read the biography on page 705, then read the entire poem.

1. What quality of snow does the poet emphasize in her first five lines?

2. What similes does the poet use to describe how the snow falls?

3. What will happen to each of the objects and places listed below once the snow falls?

   buildings:

   sharps:

   dark, worn, noisy narrows:

   streets:

   cars:

4. Look up the word *manna* if you don't know what it means. How does the final image of the poem echo the first stanza?

Name Class Date

Blackberry Eating
by Galway Kinnell

Read the short biography on page 705, then read the entire poem.

1. What activity does the speaker of the poem describe in lines 1-3?

2. What do you think the speaker's mood is? What clues does his choice of language give you?

3. What reason does the speaker suggest for the blackberries' prickly stems?

4. What does the poet compare the feel of blackberries on the tongue to?

5. What are the "peculiar words" the poet refers to?

Auto Wreck
by Karl Shapiro

Read the biography on page 711 and the Reader's Note on page 712. Then read the entire poem, answering the questions below.

1. In the first fourteen lines, the poet creates a sense of motion and urgency. List a few of the words he uses to do this.

2. How do the activities of the police contrast with the mood established in the first fourteen lines of the poem?

3. How do the bystanders respond to the accident?

4. What other forms of death does the poet compare the auto wreck to?

5. What effect does the auto wreck have on the *denouement*, or plot resolution? What do you think the poet means by this?

Name Class Date

Eyes
by Maxine Kumin

Read the short biography on page 711, then read the entire poem.

1. Where and at what time of day does this poem take place?

2. Who or what is Amanda? What simile does the poet use to describe Amanda's eyes in the dark?

3. What circumstances have made it impossible for the speaker to sleep?

4. Who or what are the four victims in stanza four? What is happening to each?

5. What does the speaker ask Amanda to do?

Losses
by Randall Jarrell

Read the biography on page 711, then answer the questions below.

1. Who are the people referred to by the pronoun *we* in the poem?

2. What do you think the poet means by the line "We died like aunts or pets or foreigners"?

3. How did the lives of the people in the poem suddenly change?

4. How were the people in the poem finally the same as those they bombed?

5. What do you learn about the people the poet refers to by the pronoun *they?* Write a brief portrait of "them."

Name Class Date

To Be in Love
by Gwendolyn Brooks

Read the short biography on page 716, then read the entire poem.

1. What is the subject of this poem?

2. What are some of the things characteristic of love as presented in this poem?

3. Why can't the speaker look into her lover's eyes?

4. What makes her arms turn to water?

5. What do you think the poet means by the lines "you are free/With a ghastly freedom"?

6. What does the speaker fear will happen to the "Column of Gold"?

One Art
by Elizabeth Bishop

Read the biography on page 716 and the entire poem.

1. Why is the art of losing things easy to learn, according to the speaker?

2. What advice does the speaker give in the second stanza?

3. In escalating the art of losing, what does the speaker next mention as being good things to lose? (lines 7-9)

4. Do you really think the speaker's final loss was as easy as she makes out? Why or why not?

5. What refrain can you find in this poem?

Name Class Date

Night Journey

by Theodore Roethke

Read the biography on page 716, then read the entire poem.

1. What is the setting of the poem?

2. Below are several pairs of words. Find each pair in the poem, then fill in the blanks with the word that describes what kind of language each pair represents.

   earth/berth

   mist/rest

   knees/feel

   swing/ravine

   blazing/bright

3. How does the poet feel about the country he travels through? How do you know?

4. List as many words as you can find that the poet uses to create a sense of motion.

5. Write a short poem that uses bursts of language and imagery to evoke the feeling of a trip you have made.

. . . and the old woman gathered (The Gospel Singers)

by Mari Evans

Read the biography on page 716, then answer the questions below.

1. What event does this poem describe?

2. Who are the major subjects of the poem?

3. What figure of speech does the poet use to describe the women standing together? What is the image of?

4. What qualities does the singing have?

Name Class Date

A House of Readers
by Jim Wayne Miller

Read the biography on page 721, then read the entire poem.

1. What are the people in this poem doing?

2. What simile does the poet use to describe Ruth and Fred?
   Ruth:
   Fred:

3. What simile does the poet use to describe the narrator's role?

4. What do you think the mood of the poem is? Find evidence in the poem's use of language and imagery to support your answer.

5. Describe the extended metaphor the poet uses in the poem.

Words
by Vern Rutsala

Read the short biography on page 722, then read the entire poem.

1. What does the first sentence of the poem refer to?

2. What feelings do the words create in the "we" of the poem?

3. What kind of words do the speaker and his family need?

4. Why is the choice of the word *ghosts* meaningful in the context it is used in?

5. List all the words and phrases used to represent something absent in the lives of the speaker and his family.

6. What do the people in the poem come to love, and why?

Name Class Date

How I Learned English
by Gregory Djanikian

Read the biography on page 722, then read the entire poem.

1. Where do the events of the poem take place?

2. What method does the poet use to relate the events of the poem?

3. What do you learn about the main character—the poem's narrator?

4. Briefly describe the incident that causes everyone on the team to break up laughing.

5. What two things does the narrator remember as being important to him then?

6. How do you think the narrator now feels about the experience described in the poem? Support your answer from the text.

My Father and Myself Facing the Sun
by Lawson Fusao Inada

Read the short biography on page 726, then read the entire poem.

1. Who are the two figures who appear in the first four lines of the poem?

2. In what ways are these two alike?

3. In what ways are they different?

4. What do the two men do at dusk?

5. Briefly describe the mood of the poem.

Name Class Date

The Morning My Father Died, April 7, 1963
by James Masao Mitsui

Read the biography on page 726, then read the entire poem.

1. Who is the speaker of this poem?

2. What time of day is it?

3. What two images does the poet include in the first sentence of the poem?

4. The poet uses the senses to create the feeling of the garden. Fill in the blanks below with examples of language appropriate to each heading.

   sight:

   sound:

   smell:

5. What does the speaker compare his thoughts to?

6. Do you think you would know what had happened in the poem without having read the title? Why or why not?

The Stalker
by N. Scott Momaday

Read the short biography of Momaday on page 726, then read the entire poem.

1. Who is the stalker?

2. What action is described in the first two lines of the poem?

3. How does Sampt'e regard the arrow once it has landed?

4. Why does Sampt'e think the arrow might take flight again?

5. List all the verbs in the poem that describe movement.

Name Class Date

Preface to a Twenty Volume Suicide Note
by Imamu Amiri Baraka

Read the biography on page 726, then read the entire poem.

1. What happens to the speaker when he goes outside to walk the dog?

2. What happens to the speaker when he runs for the bus?

3. What do you think is really happening to the speaker?

4. What do you think the speaker's daughter is doing?

5. How do you think the speaker feels about this?

Prayer to the Pacific
by Leslie Marmon Silko

Read the biography on page 731, then read the entire poem.

1. Where is the speaker's land? Where does she journey to?

2. What does the speaker compare the ocean to?

3. Where was the ocean born, according to the speaker?

4. What does the speaker bring to the ocean?

5. What myth does the speaker tell in Section 4 of the poem?

6. How do the old people explain the rain?

7. In what sense do you think this poem is also a prayer?

Name Class Date

Running It Backward
by John N. Morris

1. Read the entire poem. Using your own words, write as brief a description as you can of the action in the first eleven lines.

2. Where is the man going that the speaker does not wish to follow?

3. What event is described in lines 34-48? What does the speaker foresee happening next?

4. What does the "fury of flapping and clicking" refer to?

October Tune
by Joseph Brodsky

1. Read the entire poem. What three images appear in the first stanza?

2. What contrast does the poet create in the second stanza?

3. How do you think the person appearing in the second stanza affects the speaker?

Mirror
by Sylvia Plath

1. Read the entire poem. What point of view is it written from? Who or what is speaking?

2. What transformation takes place in line 10?

3. Why are candles and the moon called liars?

4. How does the woman in the poem feel about growing old? Explain.

Name Class Date

History
by Gary Soto

Read the short biography on page 736, then read the entire poem.

1. What images does the poet use in the first eleven lines to establish the poem's mood?

2. List the three things the grandmother does after her husband leaves for work, in the order in which she does them.

3. What does the grandmother do at the market? How does she feel about what she does?

4. What kind of work did the grandmother do in the 1950s?

5. What things does the narrator of the poem know about his grandmother's life? What things doesn't he know?

My Father's Song
by Simon Ortiz

Read the biography on page 736, then read the entire poem.

1. What mood does the poet establish in the first seven lines?

2. What does the speaker miss about his father?

3. What literary technique does the poet use from line 8 through to the end? Who is speaking now?

4. What were the speaker's father and grandfather doing together at the time of this memory?

5. What do the father and grandfather find?

6. How do you think the poet feels about this incident? Use the text to support your answer.

Name Class Date

Grudnow

by Linda Pastan

Read the biography on page 736, then read the entire poem.

1. Who is the central figure of the poem?

2. Why did the speaker's grandfather leave the town he came from?

3. What images does the poet use to describe the desolation of the place her grandfather came from?

4. According to the speaker, what would have happened to her if she had been born in the same place? Why?

5. What does the speaker describe in the last six lines of the poem?

6. What do the grandfather's actions in the last lines of the poem become a metaphor for?

My Mother Pieced Quilts

by Teresa Paloma Acosta

Read the biography on page 736, then read the entire poem.

1. What does the speaker of the poem wonder about the quilts her mother made?

2. To what are the frayed edges of the cloth compared?

3. List as many different kinds of cloth as you can that are of significance to the history of the family in the poem.

4. What are the two metaphors the poet uses to describe the mother and her sewing in lines 37-43?

5. What emotional effect does the quilt have on the speaker?

Name Class Date

Easter

by Garrison Keillor

Beginning the Selection

Read the biography on page 742. Then read the story through the paragraph where Barbara and Ruthie sit "in the yard talking about child rearing" (page 744, column 1). Answer the questions below as you read.

1. What animal does Father Emil feel the people in the pews at Our Lady usually resemble?
2. How were the churchgoers different this past Sunday morning?
3. What is it that the narrator imagines Death will say to him?
4. According to the narrator, what do grandparents forget about children?
5. What does her grandson Doug ask Virginia Ingqvist about buildings?
6. What is the major cause of injury to children, according to the narrator?

Continuing the Selection

Read the selection to the end, answering the questions below.

7. What is ironic about Grandma Tollefson saying to her grandson, "I could hear him so clear, just like I can hear you"?
8. What does Mr. Buehler find the birthday boy and his friends doing when he peeks in on them?
9. What simile does Keillor use to describe Mr. Buehler's 1950s hairdo?
10. What simple event does the narrator remember that illustrates the philosophy "Nothing you do for children is ever wasted"?

Thinking About the Selection

11. Garrison Keillor finds humor and significance in the most seemingly ordinary events. Think of something that happened to you in the past week that could be written about in a humorous way. Write it on another sheet of paper.

Name Class Date

from The Lonely Hunter

by Virginia Spencer Carr

Beginning the Selection

Read the selection through the last paragraph in column 1, on page 750. Answer the questions below as you read.

1. What is Carson like at the start of her first voyage away from home?

2. Why was the arrangement with pen pal Claire Stasser an unfortunate one?

3. How does Carson feel about New York City, once she has arrived there?

4. During what period does Carson's life in New York City take place?

Continuing the Selection

Continue reading the selection through to the end, answering the questions below.

5. Make a list of the different jobs Carson held. How successful was she at them?

6. How does Carson meet her new friend?

7. List the sights and sounds of the wharves, both by day and by night.

   sights:

   sounds:

8. What emotions do the wharves arouse in Carson?

Thinking About the Selection

9. How do you think Carson changed during her time in New York City? Answer the question on a separate piece of paper.

Name Class Date

from Blue Highways

by William Least Heat Moon

Beginning the Selection

Read the biography on page 754. Then read the selection to the space on page 758, column 2.

1. Why does the author find that the roads make for "hard driving" on his first day out?

2. What resolution does the author make about the roads he is going to travel? Where does the name "blue highways" come from?

3. What is the name of the van that the author drives?

4. Briefly describe the author's encounter in Shelbyville, Kentucky. What does the author end up envying?

5. Where is the first place the author feels at rest?

Continuing the Selection

Continue reading to the end, answering the questions below.

6. What system does the author use to find "honest food at just prices"?

7. Although the author describes the people he meets, his interactions also reveal something about himself. What do you learn about the author at the City Café in Gainesboro, Tennessee?

8. How did the town of Nameless get its name?

9. How does the Watts family treat the author?

Thinking About the Selection

10. How do you think the author has changed from the time the selection begins to the time he leaves Nameless? Answer the question on a separate sheet of paper.

Name Class Date

from **Hunger of Memory**

by Richard Rodriguez

Beginning the Selection

Read the biography on page 764. Read the selection to page 766, column 1, the paragraph that begins "What *did* I see in my books?"

1. How do the author's parents regard reading? What do they read?

2. What were some of the author's confusions and reservations about reading?

3. How does the author conquer the "fear of the silence" that he felt when he read?

4. When the author embarks on his serious program of reading, what conflict does he encounter at school and at home?

Continuing the Selection

Continue reading the selection to the end, answering the questions.

5. In the passage where the author describes his pleasure in reading, list some of the language the author uses to evoke that mood.

6. What were some of the books the author enjoyed the most? What did he like and dislike about these books?

7. What do you think the author means when he writes, "I was not a good reader"?

Thinking About the Selection

8. On a separate piece of paper, write about a book that has had particular meaning for you.

Name Class Date

from **To Be Young, Gifted and Black**

by Lorraine Hansberry

Beginning the Selection

Read the biography on page 769. Then read the selection through to the end of Section 7, answering the questions below.

1. What impulse does the author describe in the first section?

2. What do you learn about the author and her family in Sections 3 and 4?

3. In Sections 5 and 6, the author describes some memories from her early childhood. What are those memories of, and how do they make her feel?

4. Draw a brief portrait of the author's father, using your own words.

Continuing the Selection

Continue reading the selection to the end, answering the questions.

5. Who has written the letter in Section 8, and to whom was it sent?

6. What does the author's father spend many years of his life, his talent, and his money fighting?

7. How did her father's struggle directly affect the author's life?

8. What was the outcome of the legal battle fought by her father?

Thinking About the Selection

9. Some of the language used by the author is heavily ironic. Find the words you think the author means differently than their actual meaning would suggest. Do you think her ironic tone works well? Use another sheet of paper to answer the questions.

Name Class Date

from **Shadow and Act**

by Ralph Ellison

Beginning the Selection

Read the biography on page 775, then read the selection to page 777, column 1, the end of the paragraph that begins "I recall an odd conversation with my mother during my early teens. . . ."

1. What must everyone learn to do with his or her name, according to the author?

2. What is especially difficult for blacks, according to the author, in making a name one's own?

3. What does the author consider a source of pride in examining the European names so many blacks bear?

4. How does the author refute the "misconceptions" of educators who trace the reading difficulties of Negro children to their Southern background?

5. What early difficulty did the author experience with his own name?

6. Who is the author named after?

Continuing the Selection

Continue reading the selection through to the end.

7. In talking with his mother, Ellison learns more about his name. Why did his father choose it?

8. Why was Ellison confused when adults called him Ralph Waldo Emerson?

9. What metaphor does the author use to describe his difficulty in dealing with his name?

Thinking About the Selection

10. Think of someone you know who has a nickname—it could be yourself. On a separate sheet of paper, explain why the nickname seems appropriate or inappropriate to you.

Name Class Date

Nobel Acceptance Speech

by Elie Wiesel

Beginning the Selection

Read the biography on page 779, then read the selection to page 780, column 1, through the paragraph that begins "Sometimes we must interfere."

1. In what way does the author feel the Nobel Committee's choice transcends him?

2. Who do you think the young boy that the author talks about in paragraphs 4 through 6 is?

3. What does the phrase "the kingdom of the night" mean to Wiesel? What did the boy discover when he discovered this kingdom?

4. What are the questions the boy asked then, and is asking now?

5. What response does the author make to the two questions?

6. What promise does the author make to himself, and why?

7. When should people interfere in the events of other lives and other nations?

Continuing the Selection

Read the selection to the end, answering the questions.

8. Besides "Jewish priorities," what other causes does the author embrace?

9. What, according to Wiesel, do the victims of oppression need to know?

10. According to the author, who else has a claim to our lives?

Thinking About the Selection

11. The author writes that "Silence encourages the tormentor, never the tormented." On a separate piece of paper, write a short paragraph explaining why you think this is—or is not—so.

Name Class Date

The Man in the Water
by Roger Rosenblatt

Beginning the Selection

Read the biography on page 782. Then read the selection to page 783, column 1, through the end of the paragraph that begins "But the person most responsible for the emotional impact. . . ."

1. What three details does the author pick out as being somewhat unusual among the commonplaces of this disaster?

2. What reason does the author offer as a possible explanation for the attention focused on the crash?

3. According to the author, who is the person most responsible for the "emotional impact of the disaster"?

4. Briefly describe the actions of "the man in the water."

5. What effect does the man in the water's anonymity have on the way people see what he has done, according to the author?

Continuing the Selection

Continue reading the selection to the end, answering the questions.

6. What makes the man in the water's "final act" so stunning to the author?

7. What "timeless battle" does the author describe?

8. Why does the author conclude that the man in the water did not, ultimately, lose the fight with nature?

Thinking About the Selection

9. Which of the people in this selection do you think you would most resemble in a crisis—the man in the water, the rescuers, or those who accepted the rope and ring? Answer on another sheet of paper.

Name Class Date

The Red Badge of Courage: Chapters 1 and 2

by Stephen Crane

Beginning the Story: Chapter 1

Read the background information on pages 793 through 795. Then read all of Chapter 1. Answer the questions that follow as you go along.

1. On which side are the men in this army fighting?

2. Describe the interaction between the loud soldier and the tall soldier.

3. What does the character who is introduced as "the youthful private" do when he hears that the army is going to fight the next day?

4. The young private once thought of war as "crimson blotches on the pages of the past." Why does he now distrust the war in his country?

5. Find and describe the flashback that occurs on pages 798 to 799.

6. What is the problem with which the youth, Henry, struggles?

7. When Jim, the tall soldier, tells the youth he would fight if everyone else fought and run if everyone else ran, why is Henry relieved?

Continuing the Story: Chapter 2

Read the entire chapter, answering the questions below.

8. What is the outcome of the rumor that Jim had been spreading?

9. What two opinions about his comrades' courage does the youth waver between?

10. The men march in the dark. As the sun comes up, what do the two columns of men look like to the youth?

11. What is the nature of the disagreement between Henry and the loud soldier?

Thinking About the Chapters

12. Find and discuss on another sheet of paper the passages that show Henry as isolated from his comrades.

Name Class Date

The Red Badge of Courage: Chapters 3 and 4
by Stephen Crane

Continuing the Story: Chapter 3
Read Chapter 3 only, answering the questions below.

1. In what ways has the regiment lost the marks of a new command? In what ways is it still identifiable as an untried regiment?

2. Find the paragraph in this chapter that marks the change in the regiment's combat state. Write the first fourteen words below.

3. How does the youth feel once he realizes that "the time had come"?

4. When the youth scrambles up the bank, what does he see instead of the expected grand battle scene?

5. How does the landscape appear to Henry after seeing the dead soldier?

6. How does Henry react to being marched "from place to place with apparent aimlessness"?

7. How does the loud soldier betray his fears to the youth?

Continuing the Story: Chapter 4
Read the entire chapter, answering the questions below.

8. What opposing views of the progress of the battle are presented by the rumors that fly among the new regiment?

9. Why do the men laugh when the lieutenant is shot in the hand?

10. What resolution does the youth make on seeing the fleeing regiment?

Thinking About the Chapters
11. On a separate piece of paper, describe the battle situations the youth confronts in the two chapters you have just read.

Name Class Date

The Red Badge of Courage: Chapters 5 and 6

by Stephen Crane

Continuing the Story: Chapter 5

Read the entire chapter. Answer the questions as you go along.

1. To what sensation does the youth compare the feeling he has while waiting for the battle to begin?

2. Below is a list of similes used by the author in this chapter. In the blanks, fill in the object the comparison describes.

   ". . . as if seven hundred bonnets were being tried on.":

   ". . . like a wet parrot.":

   ". . . like that of a weeping urchin.":

   ". . . like a firework.":

3. Once the battle begins, how does the youth feel in relation to his companions?

4. How does the regiment respond when it seems as though they have held the enemy back? How does Henry respond?

5. As he gazes at the pure, blue sky and the sunlight on the trees and fields, what surprises Henry?

Continuing the Story: Chapter 6

Read the entire chapter, answering the questions below.

6. What surprise is in store for the regiment after this initial victory?

7. How do the youth and his fellow soldiers respond when they discover the battle is not yet over?

8. Briefly describe the point in the chapter when the regiment begins to run.

9. How does Henry feel toward the other regiments who remain fighting and toward the general still directing the battle?

Thinking About the Chapters

10. On a separate sheet of paper, describe the shift in the youth's mood from the start of Chapter 6 to the end of the chapter.

Name Class Date

The Red Badge of Courage: Chapters 7, 8, and 9

by Stephen Crane

Continuing the Story: Chapter 7

Read the entire chapter, answering the questions below.

1. What information does the youth learn at the start of Chapter 7? How does this information make him feel?

2. What incident does the youth use to rationalize the fact of his fleeing from battle?

3. What sight makes the youth turn and run again?

Continuing the Story: Chapter 8

Read the entire chapter. Answer the questions below.

4. Henry hears "a crimson roar" in the distance. Why does he now run toward the fighting he has so recently escaped?

5. What does the youth realize about the new battle taking place?

6. As Henry views the battle, what metaphor does Crane use to describe war?

7. Describe the interaction between the youth and the tattered man.

Continuing the Story: Chapter 9

Read the entire chapter, answering the questions below.

8. What is the source of the youth's shame as Chapter 9 begins?

9. What does the phrase "red badge of courage" refer to?

10. Who does the "spectral soldier" turn out to be? What do you remember of this soldier's actions earlier in the novel?

11. What is Jim Conklin's greatest fear?

Thinking About the Chapters

12. On a separate sheet of paper, compare and contrast the youth's responses to death in Chapters 7 and 9.

Name Class Date

The Red Badge of Courage: Chapters 10 and 11

by Stephen Crane

Continuing the Story: Chapter 10

Read Chapter 10, answering the questions below.

1. What amazes the tattered man about Jim Conklin's death?

2. What fear does the youth soon develop about his companion, the tattered man?

3. Who is Tom Jamison? How does he figure in this chapter?

4. What is the question asked by the tattered man that makes the youth angry?

5. Why does the youth leave the tattered man wandering in the field?

6. How does the youth feel about himself at the end of this chapter?

Continuing the Story: Chapter 11

Read the entire chapter, answering the questions below.

7. What is the mood in the first few paragraphs of this chapter?

8. When he sees the army retreating from the battle, what is Henry's response?

9. What event causes the "black weight of his woe" to return to the youth? Why?

10. What does the youth contemplate doing when he sees the men marching into battle?

11. What outcome does the youth see for himself should his side win or lose the battle?

Thinking About the Chapters

12. On a separate piece of paper, describe Henry Fleming—his doubts, fears, ambitions, etc.

Name Class Date

The Red Badge of Courage: Chapters 12 and 13
by Stephen Crane

Continuing the Story: Chapter 12
Read the entire chapter, answering the questions below.

1. What happens to the column that the youth has only recently seen marching into the heart of the conflict?

2. What phrases does the author use to refer to war?

3. What happens to Henry when he grabs one man to ask why he is running?

4. What past events come into Henry's mind as he walks along?

5. What does the cheery man do that characterizes him as cheery?

6. How do Henry's encounters with the tattered man and the cheery man differ?

Continuing the Story: Chapter 13
Read all of Chapter 13, and answer the questions below.

7. What story does Henry give Wilson when he arrives in camp?

8. As the corporal inspects Henry's wound, what irony can you find in his assessment?

9. Briefly describe the scene that the youth encounters around the campfire. What mood do you think the author creates in this scene?

10. Who finally helps Henry? What does he do to ease Henry's state?

Thinking About the Chapters

11. Imagine that you are the loud soldier, Wilson, writing a letter home. On a separate piece of paper, describe your encounter with Henry.

Name Class Date

The Red Badge of Courage: Chapters 14, 15, and 16
by Stephen Crane

Continuing the Story: Chapter 14
Read the entire chapter, answering the questions below.

1. As the youth looks at the sleeping men around him, what thought flashes through his mind?

2. What change does the youth observe in the behavior of his friend Wilson?

3. What incident takes place that confirms the changes in Wilson?

4. Do you think Wilson has any idea that Henry ran from battle?

Continuing the Story: Chapter 15
Read the entire chapter. Answer the questions below.

5. How does Henry regard the yellow packet entrusted to him by his friend?

6. How does he feel now about the oncoming battle?

7. What is Henry's feeling about himself at the end of this chapter?

Continuing the Story: Chapter 16
Read all of Chapter 16, and answer the remaining questions.

8. What mood settles upon the regiment as it awaits its orders?

9. What effect does the sarcastic man's words have on the youth?

10. What causes the lieutenant to tell his men to shut up?

Thinking About the Chapters

11. What changes does Henry undergo while waiting to go back into battle?

Name Class Date

The Red Badge of Courage: Chapters 17, 18, and 19

by Stephen Crane

Continuing the Story: Chapter 17

Read the entire chapter. Answer the questions below.

1. Where is the youth when this chapter opens?

2. What feelings does the youth have toward the enemy?

3. Why do the men look at Henry in "awestruck ways"?

4. In what way has Henry "slept and, awakening, found himself a knight"?

Continuing the Story: Chapter 18

Read Chapter 18, answering the questions below.

5. Where do the youth and his friend go at the start of this chapter?

6. What do the two men learn about their new orders, and how do they learn it?

7. What secret knowledge do Fleming and Wilson possess?

Continuing the Story: Chapter 19

Read the entire chapter, answering the questions.

8. What does the regiment encounter when it lurches forward toward the enemy line?

9. Briefly describe the situation on the battlefield referred to below. "The faces of the men, too, showed a lack of a certain feeling of responsibility for being there. It was as if they had been driven."

10. What is the object of the struggle between the youth, his friend, and the corpse?

Thinking About the Chapters

11. How do Henry's actions in this battle differ from those of his first battle? Answer on a separate sheet of paper.

Name Class Date

The Red Badge of Courage: Chapters 20, 21, and 22

by Stephen Crane

Continuing the Story: Chapter 20

Read Chapter 20. Answer the questions that follow.

1. What duty does the youth take over at the start of Chapter 20?

2. What is the condition of the youth's regiment as this chapter opens?

3. This chapter closes with the line "The impetus of enthusiasm was theirs again." What circumstances lead to this change in the regiment's fortunes?

Continuing the Story: Chapter 21

Read the entire chapter. Answer the questions.

4. Once the regiment has returned to their own lines, what astonishes the youth when he contemplates the action just completed?

5. Briefly describe the general's reaction to the regiment's most recent battle.

6. How does the regiment respond to the general's criticisms?

7. What happens to change Fleming and Wilson's feelings about the general?

Continuing the Story: Chapter 22

Read the entire chapter. Answer the remaining questions.

8. What is the youth's mood at the start of this chapter?

9. How many regiments can Henry see fighting?

10. What thoughts strengthen the youth's—and perhaps the whole regiment's—resolve not to yield to this new assault by the enemy?

Thinking About the Chapters

11. On a separate piece of paper, characterize the condition of the regiment at the end of this most recent battle.

Name Class Date

The Red Badge of Courage: Chapters 23 and 24
by Stephen Crane

Continuing the Story: Chapter 23
Read the entire chapter. Answer the questions below.

1. What surprises the youth about the men's response to the call to "charge 'm!"?

2. What great feat does Wilson, the youth's friend, accomplish?

3. What event provides the climax of this chapter?

4. How would you describe the youth's mood at the end of this chapter?

Continuing the Story: Chapter 24
Read this final chapter, answering the questions below.

5. What circumstances does the opening paragraph of Chapter 24 describe?

6. What change does the youth begin to undergo once he realizes the battle is over?

7. How does the youth regard his flight from his first battle now, from his new perspective as a seasoned fighter?

8. What memory looms to haunt the youth? Why does it torment him?

9. How does Henry finally reconcile his treatment of the tattered soldier?

Thinking About the Story
10. The author writes of the youth, ". . . as he trudged from that place of blood and wrath his soul changed." On a separate piece of paper, discuss whether you believe Henry has changed since the beginning of the novel.

Name Class Date

Four Meetings
by Henry James

Beginning the Story

Read the biography of Henry James on page 795. Then read Section I through to the end. Answer the questions below.

1. Describe the setting and circumstances of the narrator's first meeting with Miss Caroline Spencer.

2. Briefly describe Miss Caroline Spencer.

3. What has Caroline Spencer been diligently saving her money for?

4. In what way does Caroline Spencer think herself crazy?

5. According to the narrator, what is the "native American passion"?

6. What has been her "great wickedness," according to Caroline?

Continuing the Story

Read Section II through to the end, answering the questions.

7. Briefly describe the setting and circumstances presented in the first paragraph of the second section.

8. Where does the brother-in-law recognize Caroline Spencer from?

9. What is Miss Caroline Spencer's mood as the narrator speaks to her about Europe?

10. What is Miss Spencer's cousin doing while she and the narrator talk?

11. What accounts for the "tiny gleam of apprehension" that the narrator observes in Miss Caroline Spencer's eyes?

12. What opinion of Caroline Spencer's cousin does the narrator form?

Name _______________ Class _______________ Date _______________

Read Section III through to the end. Answer the questions below.

13. How has Caroline Spencer's mood changed since Section II?

14. What "bad news" has Caroline Spencer's cousin given her?

15. What is the Countess's story, and what effect does it have on Caroline Spencer?

16. What is the narrator's response when he hears that Caroline is returning home?

Read Section IV through to the end, answering the remaining questions.

17. What circumstances take the narrator back to Grimwater five years later?

18. How does the minister's wife regard Caroline Spencer's visitor, the Countess?

19. How has Caroline Spencer's appearance changed since the narrator last saw her?

20. What is the cause of Caroline Spencer's distress on seeing the narrator?

21. Briefly describe the relationship between the Countess and Caroline Spencer.

22. What is ironic about the story's very last sentence?

Thinking About the Story

23. At the beginning of the story, the narrator writes of Caroline Spencer, "I am very sorry to hear of her death; and yet . . . why should I be sorry?" Do you share the narrator's viewpoint? Explain why or why not on a separate sheet of paper.

Name Class Date

Afterward
by Edith Wharton

Beginning the Story

Read the biography of Edith Wharton on page 817. Then read the story through to the end of Section I. Answer the questions below.

1. What literary technique does the author use to open this story?

2. In what country does the story take place?

3. Who are the Boynes and what are they looking for?

4. What peculiar characteristic does the ghost haunting Lyng exhibit?

5. What has brought about the Boynes' sudden change in fortune?

6. What is the appeal of their new home, for the Boynes?

7. What concerns about her husband begin to affect Mary Boyne?

8. What has Mary Boyne been able to find out about the ghost from the villagers?

9. What incident does Mary Boyne eventually recall that might possibly be a visit from a ghost?

10. What is Ned's explanation for the identity of the man he and Mary saw?

11. In what way does Mary's "discovery" of the ghost fit Alida Stair's description?

Continuing the Story

Continue reading the story to the end of Section II.

12. What does the letter Mary receives contain?

Name Class Date

13. What are Mary's feelings about the way in which she has participated in her husband's career?

14. Why has Elwell withdrawn his lawsuit, according to Ned Boyne?

15. What do you think of Ned's explanation to Mary concerning Elwell's lawsuit?

Read the story to the end of Section III, answering the questions.

16. What part does the house play in Mary's mood the next morning?

17. Briefly describe the visitor who comes looking for Ned Boyne.

18. What occurrence causes Mary Boyne great distress?

19. Who did Ned Boyne leave the house with?

Continue reading the story to the end of Section IV.

20. What irony occurs to Mary at the start of this section?

21. What is the only information to emerge during the search for Ned?

22. Does Mary expect to see Ned again?

Read the story to the end. Answer the questions below.

23. What does Mary discover from Parvis about her husband and Robert Elwell?

24. Why is Mary so shocked when she sees Elwell's photograph in the newspaper?

Thinking About the Story

25. On a separate piece of paper, write the dialogue you think would have occurred between Boyne and Elwell in Boyne's study.

Name Class Date

Tom Outland's Story

by Willa Cather

Beginning the Story

Before beginning the story, read the Comment on page 839. Then read only Section I, answering the questions below.

1. What sidetracked the narrator from going to college?

2. Use your own words to briefly describe the scene in the card room of the Ruby Light saloon.

3. Examine the actions of the narrator and Rodney Blake up to the point where the narrator writes, "From that night Blake and I were fast friends." What do you learn about each man's character?

4. Why do Tom and Roddy give up their jobs on the railroad and go to work riding the range?

5. Describe two ways in which Blake looks after Tom while working on the range.

Continuing the Story

Continue reading through Section II, answering the questions below.

6. How does the setting with which the author opens Section II differ from that of Section I?

7. What does Rapp say he will fire Tom and Blake for doing?

8. Using your own words, describe the effect the mesa has on the two men.

9. What does Tom find while out hunting turkeys?

Name Class Date

10. How does Tom feel about the place where they are camped?

Continue reading the story through Section III, answering the questions below.

11. What is the "supercargo" brought to the camp by the foreman?

12. Briefly describe Tom and Blake's new cook and housekeeper.

13. What does Tom discover on his trip into the canyon?

14. What is Tom's response to what he has discovered?

15. What do Tom and Blake plan to do once their job with the Sitwell Company is over?

Continue reading the story through Section IV.

16. How do Tom and Blake finally get to the Cliff City?

17. Once Tom and Blake have their road made and build their cabin on the top of the mesa, what do they begin to do?

18. What do Tom and Blake surmise about the original inhabitants of the city?

19. Who is Mother Eve?

Read the story to the end of Section V. Answer the questions below.

20. Briefly describe the cause of Henry's death.

21. What conclusion about the demise of the tribe does Father Duchene come to?

Name Class Date

22. What hopes for Tom's trip to Washington do Tom and Blake each have?

Continue reading the story through Section VI, answering the questions below.

23. When he finally sees Tom, why doesn't the Indian Commissioner help him?

24. What advice does Virginia Ward offer Tom about people in Washington?

25. What is Tom's opinion of the Bixbys, the people from whom he rents a room?

26. When Tom returns to Tarpin, what surprising news does he receive?

27. Why does Tom compare Blake to Dreyfus?

28. When Blake says to Tom, "I'm glad it's you that's doing this to me, Tom; not me that's doing it to you," what do you think he means?

Continue reading the story to the end of Section VII, answering the questions below.

29. Why do you think that Tom goes looking for Blake the next day?

30. How does Tom spend the summer? What is his mood during this time?

Thinking About the Story

31. When Tom says, "the older I grow, the more I understand what it was I did that night on the mesa," what do you think he means?

Unit 1 The New Land

Page 1 A Spectacle of Great Beauty

1. Columbus referred to them as Espanola. They are now called the Bahamas, Cuba, and Haiti.
2. Answers will vary and can include:

trees:	lofty, never lose foliage, verdant, flourishing, covered with flowers, loaded with fruit
birds:	countless, singing, nightingale
season:	November
clothing:	green leaf, cotton, bit of silk, none

3. bits of earthenware, fragments of platters, broken glass, nails, and thongs of leather 4. "... as the most precious jewel in the world..." 5. from heaven 6. celestial people 7. Columbus thinks that the king wants to convert them to the holy Christian faith. Because the inhabitants all speak the same language, have the same manners, and understand each other, Columbus believes their conversion will be easy. 8. Descriptions will vary and can include: They are naked; the women wear leaves, cotton, or silk. They are timid, fearful of the Europeans, and use no weapons. They are ingenuous, honest, and very generous of their possessions. They believe in heaven, are not stupid, indolent, or ferocious. They do not own private property, do not use iron; have dark, lank hair, and eat a lot. The kings and princes can have up to twenty wives; etc.

Page 3 The War God's Horse Song and A Dancing Song

The War God's Horse Song

1. Turquoise Woman's son, a warrior about to enter battle
2.

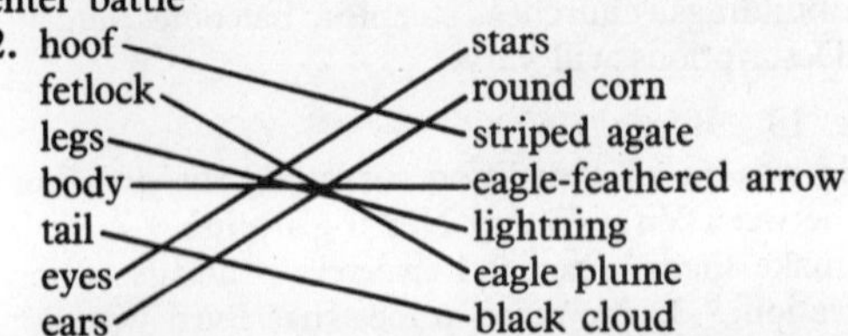

3. Answers will vary, but should include that the narrator thinks his horse has great powers and is unlike any other. 4. Answers will vary, but should get at the idea that the horse is a source of wealth to the narrator, both in what the horse can help him possess (sheep, other horses) and in the power and pleasure it brings. 5. "represent" or "be a symbol for"; reasons can vary, but should mention that the narrator strongly identifies with his horse

A Dancing Song

1. that it's a song inspired by a dance, like a dance in its movement, or meant to be danced to 2. dizzy; perhaps she, or he, has been dancing round and round 3. tadpoles 4. a blue dragonfly 5. In the dark, the dancer runs to the sounds of drumming or the sounds of the evening. 6. back to the song's first stanza, where "tadpoles sing among the reeds..."

Page 4 Firefly Song and Three Fragments

Firefly Song

1. flickering, dancing, wandering 2. light 3. to the firefly, flying through the air, its light blinking on and off 4. "once more before I sleep"

Three Fragments

1. possible answers: reflections on the water, ripples 2. a powerful dream, either good or bad; the dream has transferred its power to the singer
3. Both describe ordinary things in nature behaving in extraordinary ways. Water bugs can't draw shadows across water and bushes don't sing.
4. Answers will vary.

Page 5 from The Iroquois Constitution

1. Yes, because *confederate* means "ally" or banded together, and they are all planting the Tree of Great Peace together. 2. Atotarho and his cousin lords 3. the image of a tree (the Tree of Great Peace) 4. They cast all their weapons into the hole created by uprooting the tree, bury them, and plant the tree again. 5. It is the sign of "lordship"; it signifies that Atotarho and the cousin lords will become mentors of the people of the Five Nations. 6. He will be resistant to anger, offensive action, and criticism; carry out duties with patience; be firm but compassionate; not feel anger or fear; act with calm deliberation; cast aside self-interest; and have the present and the future in view. 8. *beads*, *tools*, *guns* should be circled 9. in the skies above

Page 6 from The Narrative of His Journey

1. Answers will vary; anything goes—from serious to humorous "genealogies." 2. hawkbells and beads 3. The boat capsized; three men were drowned; a wave carried the rest of the men ashore, naked; a north wind came down on them, bringing them close to death; they built fires and prayed. 4. They began to howl and lament at the foreigners' misfortunes; responses to the second part of the question will vary, but may include references to the Indians' ability to feel acutely the unhappiness of others. 5. The Indians carried them, "so swiftly they hardly let us touch the ground," lit fires at intervals to warm them, danced and rejoiced all night, and fed the Europeans fish and roots in the morning. 6. The Europeans believed they needed an examination and a diploma. The Indians blew on the sick, laid on hands, passed a pebble along the stomach, made a cut and sucked on the wound, and cauterized wounds with fire. 7. Answers will vary.

Page 7 Making Peace with the Illinois Indians

1. The village contains 460 lodges, thatched with mats of reeds thick enough to keep the weather out; each lodge has four or five fires, around which one or two families live on good terms. The Indians hunt in winter and hide their corn underground, which they subsist on until harvest. It is a great offense to them to disturb it in their absence.
2. He intends to find a way of paying them back, or "satisfying" them. 3. because he sees that La Salle does not intend to make war, even though he could easily win because of the Illinois' confusion
4. They negotiate peace. First, two Illinois chiefs display a peace pipe from the top of the hill; then

the Illinois on the other side of the river do the same. Finally, La Salle accepts the offer. **5.** that he took their corn and wants to exchange hatchets and things for it **6.** He wants to know if the river can be navigated all the way to the sea, and if Europeans live at its mouth. **7.** Any answers would be valid, although almost certainly there would be war between the French and the Europeans.

Page 8 The New Land

1. by the "hazard of his life" **2.** to others who might be tempted by what they read to travel to the New World **3.** 4, 1, 3, 2 **4.** "Here" is America, the New World, New England; any of these answers are correct. **5.** "Only such as with free consent may be spared": fatherless children of 13 or 14 and young married people. **6.** Answers will vary; students will weigh the hardships of the journey and life in the New World with the possibilities for wealth and personal gain.

Page 9 from The History of Plymouth Plantation

1. that this is a history of Plymouth Plantation that will tell us of the travelers' voyage across the ocean and of their safe landing in Cape Cod **2.** the story of the "profane young man" who curses the passengers, telling them they'd be thrown overboard before long; this man is stricken with a "grievous disease" and dies, becoming the first person to be thrown overboard **3.** A main beam amidships was "bowed and cracked" by fierce winds, and the boat was leaky. **4.** An "iron screw" was used to raise the beam, while a post was put under the beam and firmly bound to the lower deck. The decks and "upper works" were caulked. **5.** John Howland is thrown into the sea when the ship pitches; he grabs a halyard, which runs its full length. Howland, though many fathoms underwater, is hauled up by the rope and fished out with a boat hook. **6.** "It pleased God to smite this young man"; "they noted it to be the just hand of God upon him"; "they committed themselves to the will of God"; "it pleased God that he caught hold"; "by God's good providence they did." Answers will vary for the second part, but should be along these lines: that only by God's will do things happen; that God punishes transgressions against him; that God is always watching the affairs of humankind, etc.
7. Cape Cod; they don't land, instead, they keep sailing, hoping to land near Hudson's River. They finally land in Cape Harbor. **8.** the land, or earth
9. friends to welcome them, inns to entertain or refresh them, houses or towns to go to or to look for help in **10.** a hostile welcome; the Indians were ready to fill the Pilgrims' sides with arrows
11. storms: cruel, fierce; coast: unknown; wilderness: hideous, desolate; barbarians: wild, savage; beasts: wild; winter: sharp, violent **12.** that if the sailors do not find a safe place for the ship in time, they will turn the Pilgrims and their goods ashore and leave them **13.** According to the biography, they are Separatists who live in Leyden, Holland, where Bradford and the rest of the Pilgrims went to avoid persecution. Their "affections and love" were "cordial and entire." **14.** The Pilgrims are completely cut off from their help because the ocean stands between them and Leyden. **15.** They see themselves wandering in a "desert wilderness," delivered from an oppressor by the Lord. **16.** Answers will vary.

Page 11 Traveling in the New Land

1. Answers are open to interpretation, but some of the following might appear: **John** is quiet, knowledgeable, willing to share his knowledge, not easily startled, polite, honest. **Debb** is noisy, intrusive, amazed to see a woman on the road, a show-off, silly, and rude. **2.** Descriptions will vary: "little Leanto," "wretched bed," "Sad-colour'd pillow," are possibilities. **3.** No; she uses words like "remains" to depict the dish of pork and cabbage, and says the sauce was so purple she thought it might have been cooked in a dye kettle. The bread is crude, or "Indian." She says that she managed to get a little of it down, but that her stomach soon revolted. **4.** She has courage; even though she is terrified, she still has a sense of humor and a wry way with words. **5.** that she will drown **6.** She is referring to a baptismal bath, or a dunking in the river. **7.** She sees "armed enemies" in every tree and "ravenous devourers" in each stump.
8. calmly; with the same courage she met the crossing in the canoe **9.** She worries about being alone so far behind the guide, and about the darkness. She questions whether this is a prudent journey. **10.** The moon comes up. **11.** Cynthia, the moon goddess **12.** the second river crossing through the fearsome dark, followed by the rising of the moon, which chases night away **13.** the moon's bright face **14.** as a sumptuous city filled with buildings, churches, steeples, balconies, etc.
15. Descriptions will vary.

Page 13 Bears

1. He was on an expedition surveying the dividing line between Virginia and North Carolina. **2.** It will make them larger and sweeter; it means better cultivation. **3.** the same grapes that Byrd was referring to in the first paragraph **4.** its highly seasoned flavor *(Hautgout)*, its tasty fat that "never rises in the stomach", and the fact that it keeps well **5.** that bears are like dogs; that the Chinese esteem dog meat **6.** They eat nuts, honey, and grapes, not animal flesh (unless they have no other choice). **7.** They don't save up food for winter.
8. Students can either tell how bears kill hogs, or how they get acorns and chestnuts down from trees. With hogs, Byrd talks about a bear's imprudence; with nuts, a bear's reasonableness.

Page 15 The Trial of Martha Carrier

1. She is charged with the crime of bewitching people; she pleads not guilty. **2.** He means that even though Martha Carrier was not physically present during some of the actions she is accused of, her spirit may somehow have been present.
3. When she looked at them they were "laid" for dead; when she looked away, as long as she was touching them, they were raised again. **4.** They confessed that Carrier had made them become witches; it wasn't used because there was already enough evidence against her. **5.** Answers will vary; students should give valid reasons for their

opinions. **6.** He claims she threatened him by telling him the doctor would never cure him. Then his foot became swollen, he developed a pain in his side, and a sore in his groin that wouldn't heal. Abbot got better when Carrier was taken away by the Constable. **7.** Sarah Abbot, John Rogger, and Samuel Preston **8.** They all claimed to have attended "witch-meetings" and seen Carrier there. **9.** One meaning of the word *hag* is "witch"; *rampant* means "unrestrained, wild, or extravagant." He is saying that she is an unrestrained witch. **10.** Answers will vary, although one feature that should be mentioned is that she seems to be an argumentative woman who got into several fights with her neighbors. **11.** There is no correct answer; students will want to think about why women were more likely to be accused as witches. **12.** Students should defend themselves against an accusation made by any of the people named in this selection.

Page 17 from Sinners in the Hands of an Angry God

1. This is a sermon about sinners who are in the power of a very displeased God. Students might expect it to be full of hellfire and brimstone. **2.** to great waters that are presently held back, or dammed, and to floods **3.** God's fierceness and wrath will rush forth with unimaginable fury. **4.** as angry and very powerful **5.** sinners; his congregation **6.** He probably feels pity and fear for them; he wants to awaken them to the danger he feels they are in. He also seems to think of them as lost and wicked. **7.** a bow **8.** justice **9.** "the mere pleasure of God" **10.** spiritual enlightenment, recognition of God's power, etc. **11.** being born again; being touched by God and raised from a dark, sinful state to one of bright belief **12.** Destruction came suddenly when they didn't expect it. **13.** He compares the sinner to a spider, or loathsome insect, being held by God "over the fire." **14.** God's hand held them up. **15.** in their sleep; since awakening; attending worship **16.** They are in danger of being consumed by the flames of God's wrath. They hang by a thread over a bottomless pit full of the fire of the wrath of God. **17.** God has absolute power over us; God alone decides who lives and dies; God is very angry with sinners and may punish them harshly when least expected. Salvation is in the hands of God. **18.** Students will probably write letters supporting the idea that God need not be thought of as angry and vengeful.

Page 19 To My Dear and Loving Husband and Upon the Burning of Our House

To My Dear and Loving Husband

1. her husband, Simon Bradstreet; she loves him **2.** They are two people united as one. **3.** whole mines of gold or all the riches of the East **4.** a river that cannot quench her love for him **5.** Yes; she says that his love is such that she "can no way repay." **6.** continuing to love this fully while they live (thus creating a love that not even death can end)

Upon the Burning of Our House

1. sorrow **2.** silent, thund'ring noise, piteous shrieks, dreadful voice, fearful sound of fire **3.** God **4.** She trusts God's will and is resigned to God's acts; she doesn't understand God's reasons, but she believes they are just because they come from God. God gives all and can take back what he pleases. **5.** It means to "express discontent." Since she lived in the house through the grace of God, it was really his house. Therefore, she can't complain about losing something that wasn't hers. **6.** He has left enough for them to continue their lives. **7.** Answers can include: places where she sat or slept; a trunk, a chest, her stores (of food), her pleasant things; the guests who will never sit under her roof, eat at her table, tell stories, or talk; candles that will not be lit, marriage celebrations that will not take place. **8.** Answers may include: making an inventory of her losses; saying goodbye; remembering with fondness all the things she loved in her house; understanding that mere possessions have no meaning in the face of God, etc. **9.** that they are futile and worthless; vain, empty, and valueless **10.** for valuing "mol'dering dust" too highly; for thinking that her "wealth" was on earth; for forgetting that heaven is what she must contemplate **11.** "that mighty Architect" **12.** a house "on high," in the next life, or heaven; a house that is truly "permanent," not made of "mold'ring dust" **13.** in God's love; in everlasting life; in heaven **14.** Answers will vary, but should include references to a disdain of material things, a belief in a higher purpose, etc.

Page 21 Huswifery

1. One interpretation might be that Taylor wanted to emphasize daily living and its relationship to the spiritual. **2.** the poet as spinning wheel; God the spinner

3.

distaff:	a stick holding raw flax or wool
flyers:	they twist raw material into threads
spool:	what the threads are wound onto
reel:	it holds the finished thread
quills:	hollow reeds onto which yarn is wound
fulling mills:	where cloth is cleaned
pink:	to dye

4.
reel — my conversation
fulling mills — Thine ordinances
holy spool — my soul
swift flyers — mine affections
distaff — Thy holy Word

5. to clothe him in robes made of the cloth spun and woven in the preceding stanzas **6.** No, the God of Taylor's poem is loving. The gentleness of the weaving metaphor supports this view. Also, the narrator is not fearful but comfortable with his God.

Page 22 Upon What Base?

1. the world **2.** A lathe is a machine that turns an object so that a tool held against it can be used to shape that object; it's used to create round shapes. In the poem it is used to shape the globe. **3.** a metal foundry; a "bellows" pumps air to a furnace to keep a fire going; molten metals are poured into "casts" **4.** God; because no one with human abilities could do the things Taylor inquires about **5.** laced, filleted, ribbons, selvage, quilt ball, canopy, spun curtains **6.** the sun **7.** that whenever the sun sets in one part of the world, it simultaneously rises in another **8.** The Almighty is the one who did everything. **9.** a sense of the awe and appreciation one feels when confronted with the beauty, vastness, and great power of God

Page 23 To S.M., A Young African Painter on Seeing His Works

1. They are both of African descent, and both are artists. **2.** seeing S.M.'s works
3. lab'ring: exerting the mind with strenuous effort
intent: significance or meaning
4. Her delight in first seeing a portrait that beautifully captured the subject **5.** The beauties refer back to the first two lines of the poem; the innermost life of the subject being brought to life in the painting. **6.** that he pursue a noble path and fix his sights on creating works that will last **7.** heaven **8.** Celestial Salem **9.** seraphic, blissful wonders of the skies, exalted, splendid city, endless day, Celestial Salem, endless spring, landscapes in the realms above, ethereal plain **10.** They are able to use purer language and treat nobler themes; their art is raised to a heavenly level. **11.** balmy wings, seraphic pinions, heavenly transport
12. thrice: three times; twice six: twelve; pinions: wings **13.** shades of time, darkness, solemn gloom of night **14.** Wheatley's picture of heaven, or the works of S.M. that inspired the poem **15.** freedom to do what you want, freedom from the "shades of time," freedom from slavery, freedom to write or paint "nobler themes"

Page 25 The Wild Honeysuckle

1. addressed to: a flower, the wild honeysuckle; set in: the place where the wild honeysuckle grows, "a dull retreat" **2.** quiet, out-of-the-way places **3.** It doesn't get stepped on or torn. **4.** Any response is fine, in the following vein: shy, retiring, needing quiet and peace to thrive, a little afraid of noisy, boisterous, unthinking people **5.** Nature **6.** It has a white flower, grows in shade, and prefers moist soil provided by a stream or creek running nearby. It seems more contemplative than shy in this stanza. **7.** It will die, due to "unpitying frosts" and "Autumn's power." **8.** the flowers that bloomed in the garden of Eden **9.** "Thus quietly thy summer goes,/Thy days declining to repose." These lines describe the ending of summer, and the declining of the day. The word "repose" also evokes death, or eternal rest. **10.** He is sad, but also seems resigned to what must happen.
11. He means that you start from nothing and you are nothing when you die, so you lose nothing in between. **12.** No; he is also talking about people, who are born, live for a time, and also die.

Page 27 Moral Perfection from The Autobiography

1. moral perfection; to live without ever committing any faults **2.** While he is guarding against one fault, another surprises him; while he is not paying attention, an old habit overtakes him; and sometimes he wants to do something so badly, he can't resist the urge. **3.** He must break contrary habits and establish new ones. **4.** Sincerity, Frugality, Order, Silence, and Moderation **5.** He thinks it will be too hard to master them all at once. **6.** He makes a book, allotting each virtue a page. He rules each page, marking each column for the days, and crosses these columns with lines indicating the virtues. At the end of each day, he marks a spot for each fault he has committed during that day. Each virtue gets one week of "strict attention." By the end of thirteen weeks, he hopes to have a clean book. **7.** order; he finds it difficult to order his business because he has to mix with the world and observe others' business hours, and he finds it difficult to order his things because he is not used to it and has such a good memory that he doesn't need everything to be in order
8. He says that demanding too much of himself might make him seem ridiculous; that if he had a perfect character, others might envy and hate him, which would be inconvenient; and that a person should allow a few faults just so his friends don't get irritated. **9.** Any response is valid, but must include four virtues and a description of those virtues (precept).

Page 28 A Witch Trial at Mount Holly

1. What event: a witch trial; Where: at Mount Holly; When: last Saturday **2.** making sheep dance in an "uncommon manner" and causing hogs to talk and sing psalms **3.** They will be weighed to see if they are lighter than a Bible, and they will be tied up and thrown into a river to see if they float. **4.** that two of the accusers be subjected to the same tests **5.** Everyone who was weighed was discovered to weigh more than the Bible, both the accused and their accusers. **6.** Everyone floated except for one man, accused of being a witch, who sank. **7.** She asked to be ducked a second time; when she still floated she said that she must have been bewitched by one of the accused. **8.** He began to doubt his innocence, and said "If I am a Witch, it is more than I know." **9.** "Thinking" people thought that anyone bound and put in the water would float (unless they were all skin and bones) until their lungs filled with water. Everyone else said the women floated because of their clothes and should be tried again in the summer, naked.
10. Franklin's humorous way of describing the events of the trial indicate that he thought them ridiculous.

Page 29 What Is an American?

1. slaves of African descent; American Indians
2. from the new way of life, the new government, and new rank **3.** British Americans **4.** The goodness and flavor of them is the result of the soil and conditions they grow in. **5.** Students should include a list of other qualities that help fulfill humankind, such as families, friends, schools, art, literature, etc. **6.** He is afraid his ignorance will prevent him from properly describing his ideas.

7. They see and talk to a variety of people; their dealings with other people are extensive. They have a variety of different ways of making money other than hard labor. **8.** sagacious: shrewd and far-sighted; litigious: apt to dispute, prone to lawsuits; censure: to condemn or to judge without restraints; disquisition: a formal inquiry or discourse on a subject; uncurbed: unchecked, unrestrained **9.** They have a "ruder appearance," religion has less influence, and their "manners are less improved." **10.** misfortune, necessity of beginning over, the desire to acquire lots of land, laziness, spendthrift ways, and old debts **11.** No; he says that such people do "not afford a pleasing spectacle"; he says that discord, enmity, drunkenness, and idleness "prevail in such remote districts" and that "contention, inactivity, and wretchedness" follow. There are no "remedies to these evils"; the magistrates are no better than those they are supposed to govern. He says that "men appear to be no better than carnivorous animals of superior rank." **12.** A new group of people move into the old frontier, the frontiersmen have either prospered and become polished or have been driven off by vice or fear of the law. The newcomers finish up the improvements, and the frontiersmen go on to carve out new settlements. **13.** He was one of the few "off-casts" who "came upon honest principles" and who stayed when the next wave of migration settled the frontier. **14.** They become, after a few generations, "Pennsylvanians, Virginians, or provincials under some other name." **15.** Any list comparing people and something that shares certain characteristics with people is valid.

Page 31 The Declaration of Independence

1. that it contains a statement of freedom **2.** the system of government that tied the colonies to Great Britain **3.** position **4.** a separate and equal place in the world **5.** the obligation to declare the causes that impel the separation of the two political entities, the colonies and Great Britain **6.** things that one is entitled to that cannot be given or taken away **7.** life, liberty, and the pursuit of happiness **8.** Any other rights the student wants to include are valid; some examples might be: the right to a free education, the right to live anywhere one wants, the right to free medical care, the right to breathe clean air, the right to have a roof over one's head . . . **9. a.** secure inalienable rights. **b.** the consent of the governed. **c.** alter and abolish destructive governments and create new governments. **10.** the tendency to put up with the evils of bad government rather than to overthrow what is familiar **11.** the duty to "throw off" a government ruled by absolute despotism; one that abuses and usurps their rights **12.** the establishment of absolute tyranny over the colonial states **13.** The revolutionary aspects of what Jefferson writes are: that governments "derive their just power from the consent of the governed" and that when a form of government threatens the rights of the governed, "it is the right of the People to alter or abolish it and to institute new Government." **14.** a list of "facts," or grievances, against the King of England **15.** He asked them to give up their right to be represented in the legislature. **16.** He would call them together "at places unusual, uncomfortable, and distant." **17.** The King has declared that the colonies are not under his protection and has waged war against them. **18.** They have made a formal request to have the wrongs committed against them remedied. **19.** They have warned them about trying to "extend unwarrantable legislation." They have appealed to their "sense of justice and magnanimity." They have asked them to stop "these usurpations." **20.** a tone of firmness, resolve, and patience pushed to the very limits **21.** Responses can vary as long as they describe the King's feelings; probably of anger and frustration.

Unit 2 Literary Nationalism

Page 33 The Devil and Tom Walker

1. on a high ridge on an inlet of Charles Bay near Boston, Massachusetts **2.** The inlet lets boats come in secretly at night to the base of the hill; the elevation makes the hill a good lookout; and the gigantic trees are a good landmark, making the place easy to find again. **3.** Kidd the pirate, who was shortly after taken prisoner in Boston and sent to England, where he was hanged **4.** They are both miserly. **5.** the quality of emptiness; "forlorn-looking," "air of starvation," "sterility," "miserable," a "thin" carpet of moss "balked his hunger," "land of famine" **6.** because of stories about the Indians once holding incantations and "making sacrifices to the evil spirit" on this spot **7.** His face is covered with soot; he is dressed somewhat like an Indian, with a red sash around his body; he has a shock of black hair standing out in all directions, and is carrying an ax. **8.** They both appear to be fair and flourishing, but are rotten to the core. **9.** He has just died and is "ready for burning," according to the words of the stranger; he is going to hell. **10.** the wild huntsman, the black miner, the black woodsman, great patron and prompter of slave dealers, the grand master of the Salem witches, and Old Scratch; the devil **11.** The stranger presses his finger to Tom Walker's forehead and leaves a scorch mark that Walker can't wash off; when Tom Walker arrives home, he hears about the sudden death of Crowninshield and remembers the tree the stranger had just felled. **12.** She is never heard from again. No one knows her real fate, but there are many stories told about it. **13.** He's worried about losing his valuables. **14.** her heart and liver **15.** that in return for the buried treasure, the devil will demand Walker's soul **16.** He refuses to become a slave trader. **17.** He lends money to those who need it, but at very high rates; he exacts "good pay and good security." No, he isn't really a friend at all. He "squeezed his customers . . . dry." **18.** He becomes a "violent churchgoer" in the hopes of redeeming himself because, as Irving says, having all the good things of this world, he starts to worry about those of the next. **19.** "The devil take me if I have made a farthing." **20.** They are not shocked by it at all, having seen so many "tricks of the devil." **21.** that ill-gotten wealth is meaningless; that all wealth is useless once you're dead

Page 35 A Rescue from The Deerslayer

1. to endure everything the Indians try to do to him, without showing fear or pain **2.** They have tied the Deerslayer to a tree and are throwing their tomahawks at his head, trying to come as close to it as possible without killing him. **3.** He is afraid that because Deerslayer killed the Panther, a Huron, one of the Huron will kill Deerslayer in revenge. **4.** The Huron sneer at the Raven's throw because it is very bad; they "murmur with admiration" at Deerslayer's steadiness.

5. (R = Raven; M = Le Daim-Mose; BB = Bounding Boy)

pretentious	R
nervous/unsteady	R, BB
quiet	M
good-natured	R
excitable	BB
confident	M, BB
hasty	BB
playful	BB
middle-aged	M
intemperate	R, BB
vain	R, M
unskilled in the art	R
childish	R
proud of his skill	M, BB
brave	M, BB
hates the white man	M

6. because he has come close to killing the Deerslayer, and if he does that, the Hurons' "entertainment" is over **7.** The Huron chief would like to invite the Deerslayer to join the tribe because he is such a celebrated hunter; the tribe wants to torture and kill him for the death of their fellow warrior, the Panther. **8.** The chief wants to keep the Deerslayer alive; because these chosen warriors take pride in their skill, no one will want to kill him.
9. because the Deerslayer is at closer quarters to the muzzle of the gun and the flash of the gunpowder's explosion **10.** ondo: undo; fa'an: fawn; indivors: endeavors; arr'nd: errand **11.** the fact that the Deerslayer has not reacted fearfully to any of the trials the Hurons have set for him **12.** Bound, the Deerslayer felt hopeless; once he is set free, his mind "resumed its elasticity," and he began thinking that he would live. **13.** Chingachgook is a Delaware warrior friend of the Deerslayer's. He penetrates the Huron guard by moving so rapidly and wearing such undistinguishable war dress that they can't tell whether he is friend or enemy.
14. Great Serpent **15.** the arrival of the redcoats, the King's troops **16.** They are attacked by the British soldiers, while the Deerslayer and Chingachgook harass them from behind. **17.** He harasses them verbally and shows his contempt for their skills; he refuses to react with fear, which makes them think that, by untying him, he will betray fear; he is then free and ready to fight when Chingachgook arrives to rescue him.

Page 37 Thanatopsis

1. to anyone who, loving Nature, "holds communion with her visible forms" **2.** the outward appearance of Nature; the things you can see **3.** "a voice of gladness, and a smile and eloquence of beauty" **4.** "a mild and Healing sympathy that steals away their sharpness . . ." **5.** death **6.** the reader **7.** stern agony: possibly the death throes, or pains of imminent death; shroud: cloth that people are wrapped in for burial; pall: heavy cloth spread over coffin or hearse; narrow house: the grave **8.** They make one "shudder and grow sick at heart." **9.** Go out under "the open sky" and listen to Nature's teachings and to the still voice that comes from the earth, water, and air. **10.** the length of a human life; it is depicted as so brief that it seems to encompass only a few days
11. You will never see the sun that shines on all living things again. (or words to that effect)
12. In the first section, he speaks of how Nature can soothe and heal the heart, then he discusses the death of the person he is addressing. He switches from a comforting, uplifting tone to a rather grim, unpleasant one. **13.** He means that when you are dead, you join the other dead, even patriarchs and kings; everyone dies and is buried in the ground.
14. rock-ribbed hills, quiet vales, venerable woods, majestic rivers, complaining brooks, green meadows, and the gray and melancholy wastes of the ocean **15.** the earth—the entire planet **16.** After the death of any individual, life goes on—people laugh, plod, and chase dreams, and eventually die also. **17.** all the dead; other phrases include: the long train of ages, millions in those solitudes, tribes that slumber in its bosom **18.** He suggests dying calmly and with trust, rather than with the feeling of being hunted down or imprisoned against one's will. **19.** Answers will be very subjective and, it is hoped, insightful.

Page 39 A Psalm of Life and The Children's Hour

A Psalm of Life

1. that life is an empty dream **2.** Life does not end at the grave; the soul does not turn to dust when the body dies, but continues on. **3.** to act; to be a hero; not to be like cattle; not to trust the future; to forget the past and live in the present; to remember God **4.** the world **5.** We can learn to live life fully, and when we die our marks will be left in the world, marks that will help the ones who follow.

The Children's Hour

1. the late afternoon or early evening, between dark and daylight **2.** Alice is grave, Allegra is merry, and Edith has golden hair. **3.** They are stealing an hour of his work time—stealing the quiet he needs to think and write—but they are also stealing his heart. He turns the tables on them, holding them prisoner in his arms and keeping them in his heart forever.

Page 41 The Chambered Nautilus and The Ballad of the Oysterman

The Chambered Nautilus

1. the chambered nautilus **2.** The sea is the setting for the poem; the words in the first stanza are: ship, pearl, sail, main, bark, gulfs, coral reefs, seamaids, streaming. **3.** venturous bark **4.** Any answer is valid along these lines: In the first stanza the nautilus is alive and active. The poetry is descriptive and fantastical; the images are warm and full of life. In the second stanza the nautilus is dead and broken; there is a sense of abandonment and sorrow. **5.** It is wrecked and its inside has been opened up. **6.** Its tentacles are "webs of gauze"; it is frail. **7.** the nautilus adding onto his home, or dwelling, year after year **8.** that each year the nautilus grows a new chamber in his shell to live in and leaves the old chamber behind
9. child of the wandering sea: chambered nautilus; leave thy low-vaulted past: forsake a past that was small, too self-contained, not lofty; leaving thine outgrown shell: leaving a less spiritual past behind (to find freedom from earthly constraints); by life's unresting sea: out of life's incessant, ongoing vastness **10.** The soul must seek to build temples, "each nobler than the past," to expand and grow until it leaves the world it has known, its "outgrown shell," and is free.

The Ballad of the Oysterman

1. Setting: the bank of a river, with the oysterman's shop and boat nearby; another bank opposite the first; Characters: a tall young oysterman and the straight, slim daughter of a fisherman **2.** The daughter of the fisherman waves her handkerchief at the oysterman. The gesture is interpreted to mean "Come on over, no one's here but me."
3. because he's afraid that people will see him cross the river **4.** the allusion to Leander swimming the Hellespont to be with Hero, his beloved **5.** The girl's father has returned home. **6.** that she has tossed a pebble into the water and that the creature swimming away is a porpoise **7.** the daughter faints **8.** They both die: she never awakens from her swoon, and he gets a cramp and drowns in the river. They sell oysters under the sea. **9.** "Then up arose the oysterman, and to himself said he"; "Out spoke the ancient fisherman"; "Down fell that pretty innocent"; "and in the waves was drowned"

Page 43 from Snowbound

1. a cold, dark, silent December day **2.** less than a pale moon **3.** the coming of the snowstorm
4. "A chill no coat . . . of homespun stuff could quite shut out"; ". . .The coming of the snowstorm told"; ". . . felt the strong pulse throbbing there/ Beat with low rhythm our inland air" **5.** Answers will vary, but should probably include sad, gloomy, somber, unhappy. Words used to create that mood are: cheerless, darkly circled, sadder light, thickening sky, ominous, chill, hard, dull bitterness of cold, wintry. **6.** It takes place on a farm. **7.** the people who live on the farm **8.** the snowstorm finally hitting during the night **9.** because the familiar landscape has changed so dramatically; old familiar sights have taken on new, "marvelous shapes" **10.** sty, corncrib, garden wall and belt of wood = domes and towers; brush pile = smooth white mound; road = fenceless drift; bridle post = old man in coat and hat; well curb now has a Chinese roof; sweep = leaning tower of Pisa
11. hearth, red logs, tropic heat, merry . . . the chimney laughed, fire, drowsy, fireside, simmered, apples sputtered

Page 44 A Wish

1. Answers will vary; any variety of wishes are valid. **2.** She wishes not to be forgotten; she wants glory and fame to provide her with immortality.
3. She doesn't want death to end all that she has done while living. **4.** "like the gorgeous western light that shone/Over the clouds"; like the sunset reflects a sun that is no longer visible **5.** She asks not to be forgotten, even when she is dead and buried. **6.** the images of the grave as having "hideous arms" and of time's "dark currents" rolling over her **7.** She doesn't want to be remembered with tears. **8.** She implies that she is different from those who have been loved; her glory sets her apart. **9.** She wants fame and immortality.
10. Answers can vary; she might be a person who thinks she can perpetuate herself through fame and glory; she might be a vain person; other answers along these lines are acceptable.

Page 45 The Cask of Amontillado

1. Fortunato insulted him. **2.** He wants to punish Fortunato without being caught and punished himself. **3.** He hides his feelings, continuing to smile and act friendly. **4.** They both know about Italian wines. **5.** to emphasize that Fortunato plays the role of the fool, or dupe, in this story **6.** He plays on Fortunato's vanity by telling him that some say Luchesi's taste is equal to Fortunato's. He pretends concern for Fortunato's health. He makes Fortunato think he (the narrator) may have been deceived in buying the Amontillado. **7.** No, he's playing a game with Fortunato and enjoying it.
8. Montresor wants Fortunato to get more drunk than he already is so he can do what he wants with Fortunato. **9.** They are cold and damp and covered with nitre; they are down a long winding staircase; they are unlit; they are extensive; they are used to store wine; their walls are made of human bones. **10.** Responses will vary; perhaps he will strike him with it or build a wall around him.
11. hasty: Fortunato; deceitful: Montresor; greedy: Fortunato; manipulative: Montresor; clever: Montresor; vain: Fortunato **12.** bones **13.** Montresor chains him to a granite wall. **14.** He rattles his chains, he screams, he pretends it's all a joke, then he is silent. **15.** Responses will vary for the moods of the different settings. Possibilities are: Montresor's deserted house: large; elegant, dark; the crypt: small, dark, very damp; the catacombs: dank, cold, dark; the street: lively, dusk

Page 47 Hop-Frog

1. He's fat, oily, and dedicated to jokes, practical jokes being his favorite type. **2.** They relieved tedium at the court by giving the king something to laugh *with* and to laugh *at*. It makes him seem heartless and unlikable. **3.** They are very close and try to help each other out; they are friends because they both were taken from their own homes and given as presents to the king; their circumstances at court are similar, although Trippetta has more influence. **4.** He forces Hop-Frog to drink wine, although wine crazes him. **5.** Trippetta falls on her knees and begs the king to leave Hop-Frog alone; in response, the king pushes her away and throws wine in her face. **6.** the Eight Chained Ourang-Outangs **7.** At first they panic; then, realizing that it is enacted for their pleasure, they begin to enjoy it; finally, when they realize what is really happening, they are horrified. **8.** revenge for the injuries done Trippetta; he is paying the king and his ministers back for the way they treat people

Page 48 The Raven and Annabel Lee

The Raven

1. a student's room, in December, at midnight **2.** Lenore's **3.** Lenore is his lost love. **4.** the window **5.** "Nevermore." **6.** The narrator grows more agitated. Finally he yells, "Get thee back into the night . . ." at the Raven. In the end, the narrator feels that his soul lies eternally in the Raven's shadow. **7.** still sitting on the bust above the narrator's door, casting his shadow on the floor **8.** Answers will vary: the Raven may represent death, fate, the coldest, darkest time of year (December), or spirituality.

Annabel Lee

1. that many years ago in a kingdom by the sea, a young woman named Annabel Lee loved and was loved by the narrator **2.** "a love that was more than love" **3.** She dies from a chilling wind; the narrator blames the angels for being jealous of their love. **4.** He still loves her; their souls cannot be separated (he dreams about her, sees her eyes in the stars, and lies by her side every night).

Page 49 To Helen

1. Her beauty is like the boats of ancient Nicea that brought the wanderer over a perfumed sea to his home. **2.** anastrophe: Like those Nicean barks . . . that gently . . . the weary . . . wanderer bore . . .; rhyme: yore/bore/shore; assonance: like/Nicean, wayworn/bore; alliteration: weary wayworn wanderer; simile: thy beauty is . . . like those Nicean barks; allusion: Helen's beauty compared to Helen of Troy's beauty **3.** In the first stanza, the sea is "perfumed"; in the second, "desperate." **4.** hyacinth hair, classic face, Naiad airs **5.** "Naiad airs" refer to the graceful ways of the mythological Naiad; "hyacinth hair" is golden and wavy. **6.** Students can list any of the following: Naiad airs, the glory that was Greece, the grandeur that was Rome, hyacinth hair, classic face. **7.** Thy/hyacinth, hyacinth/classic, hair/face **8.** in a window, standing as still as a statue **9.** In the first stanza, it is Helen's beauty the poet is writing about; in the last, it is her soul he is concerned with. **10.** Lo/window; agate/lamp/hand/stand; brilliant/window/niche; Psyche/regions; see/thee

Page 50 Stanzas on Freedom

1. to men who believe themselves to be brave and free **2.** He asks how they can think of themselves as brave and free when others are chained in slavery; he asks whether people who do not feel the pain of these chains are not also slaves, slaves unworthy of freedom. **3.** He abhors it and thinks that as long as one person is a slave, all humankind is, too. **4.** They would be unfit if they did not blush or become angry about their sisters in chains. **5.** like red lava **6.** True freedom means sharing the chains of others and working hard to set them free. **7.** those who fear to speak out for "the fallen and the weak"; those who turn their backs on the truth rather than suffer hatred and abuse from others who disagree; those who shrink from doing what is right because only two or three people agree with them **8.** Answers will vary, but should include references to such devices as: "Men!" questions followed by answers, the moral earnestness of the poem, the use of archaic words ("ye," "leathern"), etc.

Page 51 Escape: A Slave Narrative

1. that it is November on a bright and quiet day; the slaves are resting about the quarters of a plantation; the narrator is planning something because he has hidden a bundle of clothing away from the house **2.** leaving the family he loves; whether to tell them his plans; the possibilities of their coming to harm because he has escaped; not knowing the way to the free state of Pennsylvania **3.** He could be flogged and sold into slavery in the far South. **4.** the liability of being sold off at any given moment to an even worse condition **5.** the north star **6.** The stranger gives him directions to get to the house of an old gentleman who could help him on the way. No, the narrator forgets the directions and decides he might get into trouble if he makes a mistake following them. **7.** No, he considers it a dangerous place to pass, as he is afraid he will be stopped or recognized by the people at the tavern; and, sure enough, a man tries to stop him. **8.** "free papers"; papers that freed slaves were given to prove their freedom **9.** that he was minding his own business and had done nothing to provoke this fellow who stops him **10.** whether he should lie and insist that he is a free man, or tell the truth and obey the laws of slavery **11.** He tells them that he has been sold as a slave from the eastern shore to a slave trader who has a work gang; the trader dies of smallpox as do several of the gang; the people in the town where the trader dies are afraid of getting the disease and do not want the surviving slaves to stay there; so the narrator decides to look for work on his own. **12.** He asks the reader to overlook the lies, to understand what the obstacles were that he had to overcome, and to understand that evil was "thrust upon" him. **13.** He is cold and wet; he has no idea which direction to set out in; when hiding in a small barn, he is tormented by a small barking dog that he fears will alert people to his hiding place; he is exhausted, afraid of pursuit, and so hungry that he tries to eat an ear of Indian corn. **14.** "Come in and take thy breakfast, and get warm. . . ."

15. Any dialogue the student writes between Pennington and his family is valid.

Page 53 Songs of America

Deep River

It's a gospel feast, the promised land, the land where all is peace.

Swing Low, Sweet Chariot

1. Home is heaven. **2.** They're looking forward to a better life after death.

Follow the Drinking Gourd

1. "the old man is a-waiting for to carry you to freedom" and "follow the drinking gourd" **2.** In the first two spirituals, the better place is over the river Jordan and found only after death; in this spiritual, the road to freedom and a better place can be traveled in this life.

The Kansas Emigrants

1. They both set out on their journeys in search of freedom; they both crossed huge expanses (the Pilgrims, the ocean; and the emigrants, the plains). **2.** He's talking about the betrayal of the ideals of freedom that slavery involves.

Clementine

1. The narrator is the man who used to love Clementine. **2.** He says he's "dreadful sorry" but he "draws the line" about being sentimental. His song has the wry perspective of someone so used to loss that he can find humor in it.

Unit 3 American Classic

Page 55 Maxims and Fable

Maxims

1. Once spoken, they will become "universal sense," others will share them. **2.** Answers may include any of the following: society: a group that works to achieve some end, or a group with common traditions and interests, or a leisure class of people who define manners and fashion; manhood: humanness, individuality, one's courage, or one's uniqueness **3.** Both emphasize being true to yourself and your own beliefs. **4.** that he lives for himself, and he doesn't intend his life to be an object of diversion or amusement for others **5.** Answers will vary but should allude to an imaginary and troublesome nonexistent thing that pesters people. **6.** He views them as small-minded, obsessed with "consistency," and afraid to think for themselves. **7.** He means that in the haste to develop and adopt innovation, humankind has forgotten the basics.

Fable

1. The mountain called the squirrel "Little Prig." **2.** squirrel: small, spry, can crack a nut, can't carry forests on its back; mountain: large, makes a good squirrel track; carries forests on its back, can't crack a nut **3.** The squirrel feels it is "no disgrace to occupy my place," believing all things have their proper place in the world.

Page 56 from Self-Reliance: A Nonconformist

1. someone who refuses to follow the established rules, customs, or ways of thinking **2.** He means the awards or approval bestowed in the afterlife, or heaven. **3.** He defines it according to his own character, his "constitution": right is what follows his constitution, and wrong is what is against his constitution. **4.** It shames him to think of it. **5.** Don't pretend tenderness for slaves in Barbados, actually show love and grace towards those near at hand. **6.** In order to do good you must sometimes offend or anger others. **7.** when his genius calls him **8.** people who are not like him in spirit, or do not "belong" to him **9.** the education of fools, the building of meetinghouses for the vain purposes of religion, charities for drunks, and "Relief Societies" for the poor

Page 57 from Self-Reliance: Traveling

10. "want of self-culture" **11.** Italy, England, Egypt **12.** The soul stays at home in the body; it doesn't need foreign places in order to expand and be nourished. Contemplation is best accomplished at home. **13.** He behaves as though he were at home; he is wise and virtuous—like a person of standing and not an "interloper or valet." **14.** art, study, or benevolence **15.** the hope of finding something greater than what the traveler knows, traveling to be amused, or traveling to find something one doesn't have within oneself **16.** They grow old in youth; they travel away from themselves. **17.** His will and mind become old and dilapidated, just like the ruins. **18.** because the traveler hopes to leave himself behind and lose his sadness; instead he discovers that he has brought his "sad self" along with him **19.** The word *giant* represents the self the author cannot escape, the same person he'd hoped to leave behind; words he uses to describe this are "sadness" and "sad self." **20.** Answers will vary; students should discuss some aspect of themselves that they've encountered—"unrelenting, identical"—on a trip.

Page 58 from Self-Reliance: Reliance on Property

21. as a lack of self-reliance; people who focus on things lack a concept of themselves or an identity; these people use things, or possessions, to define themselves **22.** A person who travels for amusement "travels away from himself"; a person who relies on property "looks away from himself and at things." Both describe people who look outside of themselves for meaning in life. **23.** He claims that people see the role of institutions as protectors of their property. **24.** They see attacks on institutions as assaults on their property. **25.** property acquired through "accident": by inheritance, by crime, or as a gift **26.** People who depend on property get wrapped up in numbers and quantities of things; thus, a single person feels "stronger" with multitudes as support; political parties are formed in much the same way. **27.** by turning inward to look at their thoughts and not looking for good elsewhere **28.** Students may list actions such as the following: church: refusal to attend church, to follow its teachings, etc.; government: refusal to obey laws one thinks are wrong, taking part in demonstrations, etc.; school: refusal to attend class, questioning accepted teachings, etc. **29.** No; just the opposite. He says "[A man] is weaker by every recruit to his banner." A person who stands alone and puts off support from those around is someone Emerson sees as being truly strong.

Page 59 from The American Scholar: Man Thinking
1. The fable is that the gods divided humankind into individual people, thinking that in this way people would be of more use to themselves and each other. The fable comes from "unknown antiquity," untold numbers of years ago. **2.** Man was divided into men in order to be of more help to himself; the division is compared to the hand, divided into five fingers. **3.** "He must return from his own labor to embrace all other laborers"; *possess* means to become whole. **4.** It is the strength that is in the "original unit," or the collective strength of humankind; it has been divided up into so many smaller units and spread out amongst such multitudes of individuals that it is diluted—"spilled into drops"—and can never be "gathered" together again. **5.** The metaphor compares the state of society to members amputated at the trunk; the metaphor says that society is made of individual "monsters," each person only a part of the whole.

6.

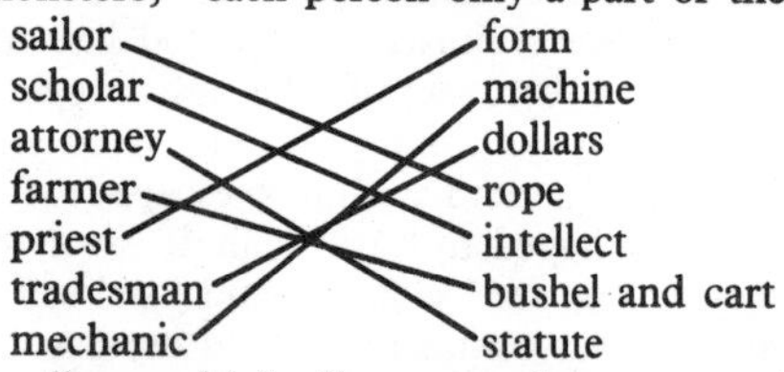

sailor	form
scholar	machine
attorney	dollars
farmer	rope
priest	intellect
tradesman	bushel and cart
mechanic	statute

7. a "mere thinker" or one who parrots other's thinking **8.** as a student or a true scholar

Page 60 Brahma
1. Brahma, the supreme soul of the universe, addresses humankind. **2.** the ways of Brahma, the Over-Soul of the universe **3. a.** far—both in distance and in time—is near; **b.** shadow and sunlight, or light and dark, are the same; **c.** those who are invisible are visible (all other gods worship Brahma) **d.** shame and fame have the same meaning **4.** that Brahma has an understanding and vastness the human mind cannot comprehend
5. The poem's tone is one of warning or rebuke; line 1 of stanza 3—"They reckon ill who count me out"—illustrates that tone the best. **6.** Even when people try to escape Brahma, they do so through Brahma's power. **7.** Brahma's "abode"; they pine to join Brahma **8.** that they can find Brahma (and have no need of heaven), because in Brahma, they will have found all **9.** Answers will vary, but should include references to the fact that it makes no moral distinctions, such as between right and wrong ("shadow and sunlight are the same"); it implies that conventional religion has no understanding of life's mysteries and fails to formulate useful moral codes ("I am the doubter and the doubt"); it draws a picture of a supreme being who is far beyond human understanding ("They know not well the subtle ways . . ."); and it states that one can "turn thy back on heaven" to find the true way.

Page 61 Days
1. days **2.** He gives them human qualities by calling them "daughters" and "barefoot dervishes"; they march, soundless, in an endless file, offering gifts and showing scorn. **3.** probably because they will not tell us what they bring; we find out only after they have departed **4.** that they whirl by, as dervishes do, chaotic and blurred **5.** singly, in an endless file **6.** because they offer each of us precious gifts (the diadems) and plain, everyday items (the fagots) to do with what we will **7.** The gifts are offered to everyone; they are bread, kingdoms, stars, and sky. **8.** He is choosing the ordinary.
9. He means that he forgot the high things that he aspired to, the sky and diadems, and explored only the small and mundane. **10.** She is scornful; because he chose the wrong gift (ignoring the expansive and lofty and choosing the ordinary).
11. Students can write any maxim along the lines that the day offers much to those who use its gifts well.

Page 62 The Snowstorm
1. "Announced by all the trumpets of the sky. . ." **2.** The snow arrives, announced by all the trumpets of the sky, and, driving over the fields, seems to alight nowhere. **3.** the image of snow that is coming down so hard every bit of air is packed with it **4.** hills, woods, river, sky, the farmhouse at the end of the garden **5.** Everyone is snowbound; they sit around the fire listening to the storm. **6.** The snowstorm is represented as a person, an architect using snow as building material.
7. the north wind, or the natural force of the snowstorm **8.** "white bastions with projected roof"; masonry made of snow **9.** It is fanciful and savage. **10.** white wreaths on a coop or kennel, forms that look like swans covering thorn bushes, lanes filled with snow, a turret over the farmer's gate, "frolic architecture" made of snow

Page 63 from Walden: Why I Went to the Woods
1. to live deliberately, to deal only with the essential facts of daily life, to reduce life to its lowest terms, learn what life had to teach, and not die without having lived **2.** They don't know whether life is stamped by God or by the devil. **3.** to emphasize, perhaps ironically, that men have assumed that they are here to glorify God without ever really thinking about what that means or considering other possibilities **4.** We live meanly, like ants; like pygmies, we fight with cranes. **5.** Instead of three meals a day, have one; instead of lots of different dishes, have only a few; have only a few businesses instead of many. **6.** a rigid economy, living simply, and aspiring to a higher purpose
7. commerce, exporting ice, riding thirty miles an hour, using the telegraph, railroads **8.** The railroad runs our lives rather than the opposite.
9. Answers will vary.

Page 64 from Walden: Why I Left the Woods
1. He felt that he had several more lives to live and that he had used up all the time he could spend on that one; he was ready to try something new. 2. Before he had been at Walden for a week, he had worn a path from his door to the pond. The analogy he draws is to the paths the mind travels, which become as worn as the path to the pond. 3. that in proportion to how much a person simplifies life, the laws of the universe appear less complex 4. "step to the music . . . he hears, however measured or far away"; follow his own inner leanings 5. perfection 6. They grew old and died. 7. His search for perfection sets time at a standstill; eons pass and cities fall to ruins around him. 8. "Say what you have to say, not what you ought." "Any truth is better than make-believe." 9. In poverty one can live life independent of possessions, experiencing what is most "significant and vital." A person who lives in poverty deals with the part of life that is most nourishing. 10. the man who lived in the tree 11. The story of the bug emerging from the table is an extended metaphor for the life that can emerge from "the dead dry life of society."

Page 65 from Civil Disobedience
1. the kind that governs least, or not at all 2. He says that the people would not have agreed to the war if they had been consulted, and calls it the work of a few individuals. 3. The government continually puts obstacles in the way of trade and commerce, and legislators, if we look at the results of their work, are no better than people who block the railroads. 4. by making known the kind of government they want 5. when that law requires an individual to be the agent of injustice to someone else 6. They should withdraw their support from the government. 7. just one honest man 8. He sees himself as the one who is free and has paid his taxes; he sees the State as half-witted, not knowing its friends from its foes, and determined to punish his body because they could not reach his spirit. He sees those outside the prison as less free than he—that they have bigger walls to break through before they can be truly free. 9. Such a state would recognize the individual as being a higher and independent power and treat the individual accordingly. 10. Answers will vary.

Page 66 This Sacred Soil
1. the signing of a treaty in which Chief Seattle gives up his people's land. 2. He is sad and resigned. 3. that the Big Chief can count on Chief Seattle to keep his word 4. Chief Seattle's people are like "the scattering trees of a storm-swept plain." The Big Chief's people are like "the grass that covers vast prairies." 5. He sees that his people receive no protection from the white people's God, while white people are protected and led by the hand. The white people grow stronger every day, while Seattle's people are "ebbing away." 6. a. The red people stay near the sacred ashes of their buried ancestors. The white people leave the land where their ancestors are buried "seemingly without regret." b. The red people's religion is given to them by the Great Spirit through dreams of old men of the tribe—it is written in the hearts of the people. The religion of the white people was written in tables of stone by the iron finger of their God. c. The red people's dead never forget the world. The white people's dead cease to love them or the land and go to wander beyond the stars. 7. He believes that soon not one of his people will remain. 8. He believes that their time of decay will surely come also, because white people cannot be "exempt from the common destiny." 9. because the spirits of all the red people who have loved the land will come back to it and fill it up 10. There is no such thing as death, only a change of worlds. 11. Answers will vary.

Page 67 from Loom and Spindle
1. They were on the lowest level of society. 2. to induce them to overlook the prejudice that was felt against women who worked in the mills 3. because the corporations wanted to cut pay and to make the women pay their own room and board 4. the first time a woman spoke out in public in Lowell 5. seeing the line of women behind her as she walked out in protest 6. the day that women citizens are given the right to vote 7. in revenge for not preventing Harriet from "turning out" 8. It was small, thin, and contained about thirty pages. It was written by the mill girls, and the first issue was six and one quarter cents. 9. She says it helped the mill workers as well as the women of the rural population, who got to sample the progressive thought that was available at the time. 10. Any response that describes what the student would have done in the event of a strike at the mills is valid.

Page 69 Young Goodman Brown
1. characters: Goodman Brown and his wife, Faith; setting: Salem village; time of day: early evening; event: Goodman Brown is leaving on a journey. 2. Goodman Brown calls himself a wretch and refers to "such an errand!" He remembers the "trouble" in his wife's face, as though she were "warned" about "what work is to be done tonight." He thinks it would "kill her" to know what he is going to do. 3. No, they don't meet by chance, they have an appointment. The man says, "You are late. . . ." 4. He is about fifty years old, simply but nicely dressed, and of the same rank as Goodman Brown. He has an air of knowing the world and being comfortable with governors or kings. He looks like Goodman Brown. 5. He carries a staff that looks like a snake. It appears to move, as though it were alive. 6. Brown tells him that his father and grandfather never went to the woods "on such an errand," and that all of his family have been good, honest Christians. 7. He knows Goodman Brown's family well. He helped Brown's grandfather whip a Quaker woman, and he brought Brown's father a pitchpine knot to set fire to an Indian village. They were good friends of his. 8. He is amazed. 9. probably because the minister

is one of his keenest supporters **10.** He doesn't want her to see him on the path with the traveler for fear that she will think he has fallen into evil ways. **11.** The traveler is the devil. **12.** that she is a witch and is on her way to the same place Goodman Brown and the devil are going **13.** the minister and Deacon Gookin **14.** Faith's pink ribbon **15.** He is crazy with despair; he laughs and runs, and beckons witch, devil, wizard, and powwow to him. **16.** Any of these are correct: his dead father and mother, Deacon Gookin, the minister, Goody Cloyse, and Martha Carrier **17.** the mystery of sin **18.** He finds himself in a calm forest. The next morning he arrives in Salem. Everything is as it had been. **19.** He becomes stern, sad, distrustful of the people around him; "he shrank from the bosom of Faith," and dies in gloom. **20.** Summaries should include the following: Goodman Brown sets off on an errand, leaving his anxious wife, Faith, behind. He meets the devil. He sees Goody Cloyse with the devil. He refuses to accompany the devil any further. He sees Deacon Gookin and the minister ride by. He sees dark clouds, hears voices (among them Faith's), and sees Faith's pink hair ribbon fall from the sky. He runs into the forest. He joins the heathen throng. He and Faith are about to be "baptised" by the devil. Goodman Brown resists and finds himself back in a calm forest. He walks home and is never the same again. He is a stern, sad, distrustful man until the day he dies.

Page 71 What Redburn Saw in Launcelott's-Hey

1. city: Liverpool; street: Launcelott's-Hey; narrator: Redburn; boardinghouse: Baltimore Clipper
2. one of sadness and desperation (the children are described as "shrunken things," the warehouse is squalid, the figure is of "what had been" a woman, the wail is "soul-sickening") **3.** that he is a compassionate man with deep feeling for others
4. The response is hard-hearted and indifferent; no one will help him because everyone thinks that the problem isn't theirs. **5.** Like everyone else, Mary refuses to help; unlike everyone else, the reason is because she already helps enough people in her own street. **6.** He feels that all he has done is to prolong their misery. **7.** Any response is valid that applies this statement to a social condition that exists today.

Page 72 from Hospital Sketches

1. The Civil War has begun, and there are wounded soldiers at the Union Hospital in Washington.
2. She loves nursing, help is needed, she wants new experiences, and has to make use of her energies; furthermore, with her gone, there will be one less person at home to feed and to worry about.
3. She is sad to see her daughter go, but tells her to "go! and the Lord be with you!" **4.** Answers will vary; students may write about Alcott's seeing a man die or sitting with a boy who has pneumonia and a man shot in the lungs. The boy calls her "motherly," the man stares. She feels old and wants to help them all. **5.** He has a noble character, a tender heart, and a frank character. He is dying without "reproach, repining, or remorse." He is truly good. **6.** She finds the women silly, stupid, and having only one idea; the men she finds ludicrous, provoking, and self-important. **7.** She is at first only "threatened" with pneumonia, but grows sicker. When the matron dies of the same disease Alcott has—typhoid pneumonia—Alcott suddenly decides to leave. **8.** All answers portraying the narrator through the eyes of one of the people she nursed are valid.

Page 73 from Uncle Tom's Cabin

1. She has heard that Mr. Shelby is going to sell her child, Harry, and Uncle Tom to a slave trader.
2. to save her boy by running away with him
3. Aunt Chloe and Uncle Tom **4.** He says that it's better for him to be sold than for the whole place and everyone on it to be sold off to pay a debt. He is not willing to break the trust placed in him. **5.** how and why she went; that she is going to Canada; that she loves him; that he should be good so they can meet in heaven **6.** People who know her will not think that Eliza would run away from the Shelbys because their kindness is known to everyone; people who don't know her will think Eliza and her child are white. **7.** The Ohio River is frozen and backed up with chunks of ice that prevent the ferry from crossing. **8.** Answers will vary, but most will agree that while Mrs. Shelby may worry about what the loss of Harry and Eliza will do to their plantation, she will probably rest easy in the knowledge that Eliza is with her son.

Page 74 from What the Black Man Wants

1. immediate: to be done at once, without delay; unconditional: to be done without limitations, absolute; universal: to be applied to everyone, without exceptions; enfranchisement: the rights of citizenship, especially the right to vote **2.** society
3. that it is premature—first blacks must achieve freedom, then labor must be organized; no, he thinks that suffrage should be granted while the need for it is obvious **4.** They may have missed their chance; it may be centuries before the right moment comes again. **5.** He thinks that women should have the right to vote also. **6.** It leads to black men undervaluing themselves and feeling inferior. **7.** simple justice **8.** He thinks that the Negro should be left alone; he says that harm enough has been done through interference. **9.** He uses the metaphor of apples falling from a tree, which should not be tied onto the tree, but should be allowed to fall or remain on the tree as nature wills. Similarly, blacks should be left alone to stand or fall by their own efforts. **10.** Answers will vary.

Page 75 Ain't I a Woman?

1. She means that if everyone is making a fuss, there must be something worth fussing about; people don't argue when everything is fine. **2.** the Negroes of the South and the women in the North
3. that they were helpless and needed to be lifted, coddled, and treated delicately **4.** because she was a slave and a poor black woman who had to work and take care of herself **5.** She ploughed, planted, and gathered in the harvest as well as any man; she

worked as hard and ate as much as any man; she endured the lash of slavery as well as any man; she bore thirteen children and saw most of them sold into slavery. **6.** by saying that intelligence has nothing to do with one's rights **7.** She points out that men had nothing to do with the birth of Christ, who was born of a woman and through God. **8.** Eve **9.** Answers will vary, but will probably mention that its effectiveness may stem from Truth's rational and persuasive arguments, which are so personal and direct.

Page 76 Gettysburg Address

1. that it was "conceived in liberty" and "dedicated to the proposition that all men are created equal" **2.** whether a nation conceived in liberty and dedicated to equality can endure **3.** They gave their lives so that the nation could survive. **4.** Answers may vary; probably the work of keeping the country together or of freeing the slaves. **5.** the men who fought at Gettysburg for what they thought right **6.** to dedicate themselves to finishing the work the men who fought at Gettysburg advanced **7.** that there be "increased devotion to the cause" these men died for; that the dead "shall not have died in vain"; that there will be a "new birth of freedom"; and that government "of the people, by the people, for the people shall not perish" **8.** Answers will vary, but should include a reference to the dignified, formal, somber, and ultimately uplifting tone of Lincoln's address.

Page 77 Letter to His Son

1. George Washington **2.** He refers to Washington's nation-building efforts, which Lee sees crumbling as civil war becomes increasingly possible. **3.** It is in a state "between anarchy and war," with states seceding from the Union, and half the country lined up against the other half. **4.** *aggrieved*; it means to oppress or treat unfairly **5.** for the Union to be dissolved **6.** honor **7.** He sees secession as revolution, and he says that the framers of the Constitution intended it to be a "perpetual union," protected by guards and securities; they didn't intend for it to be broken "by every member of the confederacy at will." **8.** anarchy **9.** No, he writes ". . . a Union that can only be maintained by swords and bayonets . . . has no charm for me." **10.** He would return to his home state and "share the miseries" of his own people. **11.** in defense

Page 78 Song of the Chattahoochee

1. to the plain **2.** It has the breathless quality of haste; words used to create this tone are: hurry, run, leap, split, flee. **3.** *h*ills of *H*abersham; *r*un the *r*apid; *f*lee *f*rom *f*olly **4.** It is being urged to slow down and stay awhile; by the rushes, waterweeds, laurel, ferns, grass, dewberry, and reeds. **5.** Answers will vary, among them could be: veiling the valleys; hickory told . . . tales of shade, poplar . . . wrought . . . her shadowy self to hold; overleaning, with . . . meaning. **6.** told/manifold; overleaning/meaning; so cold/manifold **7.** quartz and stones that look like jewels—crystals, ruby, garnet, amethyst—they bar the river's way and lure it with lights **8.** They call the river to flow down into the plain and on into the sea. **9.** It brings water to the dry fields and flowers, and it turns the mills. **10.** the "lordly main," or ocean

Page 79 from Uncle Josh's Zoo: The Ant, Tall Tale, and Brag

from Uncle Josh's Zoo: The Ant

1. They work all the time, never ask for money, are cheerful, and without malice. **2.** people **3.** Even though people have by-laws and a constitution, these mean nothing. Their laws are made with holes in them big enough for a person to steal a horse and ride it through. Human legislators and judges can be bought, and they lie around waiting for the right price. **4.** that he is no better or different than the people he spoofs

Tall Tale

1. He is out hunting in the forest and is just getting ready to shoot a raccoon he has spotted in a tree. **2.** because, having heard of Crockett's reputation with a gun, he considers himself already shot **3.** what a fine shot he was **4.** Students can write any tall tale that illustrates a talent.

Brag

1. the Ohio and the Mississippi rivers and all the streams that run into them **2.** that he strikes a blow "like a falling tree," and that "every lick" he makes in the forest "lets in an acre of sunshine" **3.** Students can write any brag about themselves that follows the selection's style.

Unit 4 Variations and Departures

Page 81 I Hear America Singing and There Was a Child Went Forth

I Hear America Singing

1. blithe and strong **2.** The carpenter measures his plank or beam; the mason gets ready for work or leaves work. **3.** The deck hand sings on the steamboat deck; the shoemaker sings sitting on his bench. **4.** Each person sings only about what "belongs" to him or her—his or her own work. **5.** The image is of robust young men singing strong, melodious songs at night.

There Was a Child Went Forth

1. a child; the child goes out each day and becomes the first object he looks at **2.** images from nature—flowers, birds, and newborn animals **3.** drunkard, schoolmistress, friendly and quarrelsome boys; fresh-cheek'd girls; barefoot Negro boy and girl **4.** They are all people who live in the community that the child lives in. **5.** as quietly setting the table, mild and clean-smelling **6.** The father is described as strong, self-sufficient, manly, but also angry, unjust, and mean; he hits out at someone and offers a "quick loud word." **7.** Things beyond the child's immediate environment—spreading farther and farther away—from the distant village to the schooner, the waves, the clouds and the distant horizon.

Page 83 When Lilacs Last in the Dooryard Bloom'd

1. Abraham Lincoln **2.** lilac: blooming perennial;

star: dropping in western sky; spring: ever-returning **3.** Abraham Lincoln **4.** The mood is one of intense grief and despair. **5.** It turns from murky despair to look at the miracle of spring, to green, growing things that are delicate and perfumed. It focuses on the peace and beauty found in nature. **6.** secluded, shy and hidden, warbling, solitary, hermit, withdrawn, sings by himself, bleeding throat **7.** a song of grief and sorrow—painful, throbbing **8.** Lincoln's coffin travels across the country to Illinois for burial. **9.** It is spring; violets grow out of the debris, wheat grows from the "shroud"; the orchards are in bloom. **10.** night, cloud darkening the land, cities draped in black, crape-veil'd women, night, torches, somber faces, night, dirges, dim-lit churches **11.** Students' answers may vary along the lines that he is offering hope, rebirth, or life, in the midst of images of darkness and death. He is bringing color and life to a dark scene of death. **12.** Answers will vary, but should suggest that the speaker does not fear death, but seems, in fact, to be embracing it, calling it "sane and sacred." **13.** sadness and woe **14.** the hermit thrush **15.** Like the thrush, the poet must sing his own song for "the dead one there I loved. . . ." **16.** pictures of spring, and farms, and homes; of sunset's golden light; pictures of daily life; "all the scenes of life and the workshops. . . ." **17.** It is "excellent," "calm," and "haughty." **18.** Section 2 is a grief-stricken outpouring of pain and sadness about death; in Section 13, while the pain is there, it is mixed with awe at the beauty of the song. In Section 2, the poet is alone with his grief; in Section 13, the poet has tempered his grief through listening to the thrush's song. Section 2 is dark, murky, and pained, while 13 is full of hope. **19.** the carol of death sung by the thrush **20.** The thrush sings to death. No, it is a song of praise. **21.** Death is something to be welcomed ("Come lovely and soothing death"), something that comes to everyone. Death is "delicate," "sure-enwinding," "cool-enfolding." The thrush sings a chant of "fullest welcome" to death; death is the "strong deliveress"; the thrush sings this song to death "with joy." **22.** those who remain behind—mothers, wives, children, etc.
23. Answers will vary, but may include: comrades, bird, lilac, dooryard, spring, western star.

Page 85 What Is the Grass from Song of Myself

1. a child **2.** "I do not know what it is any more than he." **3.** flag of my disposition: woven of hopeful green stuff; handkerchief of the Lord: scented gift, dropped, bearing the owner's name in the corners; child: babe of the vegetation; a uniform hieroglyphic: sprouting alike in broad and narrow zones; growing everywhere **4.** The poet now looks at the grass as the "uncut hair of graves"; the mood shifts from a celebration of life to a contemplation of death. **5.** from the breasts of young men, from old people, from offspring taken from their mothers, from the white heads of old mothers, the beards of old men, from mouths
6. the fact that living things die and decay, and in turn nourish the living **7.** He says they are alive and well somewhere; that there is really no death.
8. the smallest sprout of grass **9.** that death leads life forward, rather than ending it; that everything continues "onward and outward"; and that death is different and better ("luckier") than anyone thinks
10. Students' answers can vary, but most will agree he has a positive, uplifting attitude.

Page 86 Bivouac on a Mountain Side, When I Heard the Learn'd Astronomer, and Sparkles from the Wheel

Bivouac on a Mountain Side

1. that it is probably about wartime, and that it takes place on the side of a mountain **2.** a traveling army halting **3.** a fertile valley in summer, spread with barns and orchards; a steep, terraced mountain side that is broken, rocky, and planted with tall cedars **4.** It is dusk or twilight. Words indicating this are: dingily, camp-fires, shadowy forms, flickering, a sky studded with stars.

When I Heard the Learn'd Astronomer

1. the learn'd astronomer; proofs, figures, columns, charts, diagrams, to add, divide, and measure
2. It makes him sick and tired. **3.** He goes outside and looks at the stars. **4.** In the beginning of the poem, the stars are abstractions—represented by charts, proofs, figures, columns, and diagrams—and are being discussed at length. At the end, the poet is looking at them in "perfect silence" in their natural, "mystical" state, and appreciating them for what they are.

Sparkles from the Wheel

1. city's ceaseless (crowd) **2.** a knife-grinder at his wheel **3.** the sad, sharp-chinned old man with worn clothes; the quiet, attentive groups of children; showers of sparkles; the purr of the grinding stone

Page 87 The Soul Selects Her Own Society and My Life Closed Twice Before Its Close

The Soul Selects Her Own Society

1. Answers may vary: She probably means company, friends, or visitors. **2.** "selects her own society" then "shuts the door" **3.** chariots and an emperor; they symbolize riches, power, worldly enticements **4.** The soul is "unmoved," unimpressed. **5.** She closes her attention (probably her attention to all others save the chosen one).
6. personification

My Life Closed Twice Before Its Close

1. that her life closed twice, but still had not closed **2.** Students can list meanings along the lines of: death, parting, ending, shutting the door on, etc. **3.** if immortality will unveil "a third event," or parting; if her life will close three times
4. death; students' responses to the second part of the question may vary **5.** that parting can be two different things, both heaven and hell, all at once

Page 88 I Felt a Funeral in My Brain

1. Event: a funeral; Setting: in the narrator's brain
2. mourners **3.** to create a sense of monotonous, repititious movement **4.** It is making the speaker's

mind go numb. **5.** the word *treading* (it is another word that emphasizes monotonous activity) **6.** The mood is the same. It is amplified by more repititious detail; the narrator's mind goes numb; the sense of despair grows. **7.** the image of mourners treading to and fro **8.** bell **9.** probably a race of people (herself and silence), but other interpretations may be equally valid **10.** The first three stanzas are teeming with people and full of sound, but in the last stanza the narrator is alone in silence. **11.** reason (or a part of reason) **12.** Most students will agree the speaker is describing the feelings leading up to (and including) a nervous breakdown or an episode of madness; the droning repititious motion of the early stanzas gives way to the solitary feeling of being "wrecked," until finally the poem climaxes with the break in reason and the fall into unknowingness.

Page 89 Some Keep the Sabbath Going to Church and "Faith" Is a Fine Invention

Some Keep the Sabbath Going to Church

1. keeping the Sabbath, or worshipping **2.** Others go to church; the narrator stays at home. **3.** a bobolink **4.** surplice, wings, bell, sexton **5.** It continues the theme of the first stanza; church for the narrator of the poem can take place outside with just as much grandeur as indoors. **6.** The others sit listening to long sermons, hoping to get to heaven in the distant future. The poet is already halfway to heaven in the outdoors, listening to the songs of the birds and enjoying the beauty of nature. She feels she is closer to God.

"Faith" Is a Fine Invention

1. religion: Faith; science: Microscopes **2.** science; she would use a microscope in an emergency, but she would trust faith only when she was sure vision was unclouded **3.** Answers will vary. She emphasizes the word probably because seeing is so important to her. She may mean seeing the real world; she may mean understanding things. **4.** Students' interpretations will vary, but should include a reference to the fact that the poet feels that science can show us things faith alone cannot.

Page 90 There's a Certain Slant of Light

1. a winter afternoon **2.** a mood of sadness and oppression **3.** the weight of cathedral tunes, or church music **4.** certain/Slant **5.** in the soul; because it is the place "Where the Meanings are" **6.** internal difference **7.** Either or both may be checked, as both apply. **8.** It is sent "of the Air" (from on high, or heaven). **9.** The landscape listens and shadows hold their breath. **10.** Cathedral, Heavenly Hurt, Seal, imperial affliction, of the Air **11.** Answers will vary, but may mention that like winter, death is thought of as oppressive and cold. Death is an end to growth, as is winter, and both are thought to be the prelude to rebirth and rejuvenation.

Page 91 I Heard a Fly Buzz When I Died

1. She is dying. **2.** The atmosphere is still, as is the silence during a lull in a storm. **3.** buzz **4.** She sees the tear-stained eyes of the people waiting for her to die; she notes their anxious wait for "that last Onset." **5.** "that last Onset" **6.** Answers will vary; it could be God or death. **7.** She has signed away her worldly goods and willed her keepsakes. **8.** The fly comes buzzing into the room. **9.** It offsets the scene, focusing attention on the ordinary present world. **10.** Answers will vary. It could mean that her sight has gone and she can no longer see—she is dead. It could mean her view of the next world has become obstructed. **11.** Because the common housefly is the smallest and most mundane of creatures; and there is irony in the fact that although it flies on blue wings it blinds her to the glory of God and the revelations expected of death. **12.** The speaker can't "see to see"—she is dead and can no longer seek the meaning of what she is experiencing.

Page 92 Because I Could Not Stop for Death

1. They ride in his carriage. **2.** personification **3.** Immortality **4.** Time has slowed down; Death drives "slowly" and "knows no haste," and the narrator has put aside all activities of a normal life. **5.** a school, children, fields of grain, and the setting sun **6.** Answers may vary. The journey could represent the move away from everything familiar—the schoolyard with the children playing and the vast fields—toward a place never before experienced. It may represent the passage of the three stages of life—from youth through maturity and aging—all leading to death. **7.** Answers may vary. The sun is going down, which may account for a chill in the air. Then, too, they are nearing the grave, a dark, cold place. She is dead and has no way of protecting herself from its chilling grip. **8.** Answers may vary. The most likely answers are: the grave, a coffin, the ground, etc. **9.** to eternity or heaven or the life after death **10.** A century becomes shorter than a day since she died, or "surmised" that she was on the road to eternity. **11.** Most students will agree that Dickinson seems to be saying that death is nothing to fear and should be accompanied with grace and a feeling of inevitability. Others may argue that these words are being used ironically—that death comes and snatches us away when we least want it to. Either answer is valid.

Page 93 The Celebrated Jumping Frog of Calaveras County

1. He suspects that his friend intended for him to have to listen to some "tedious" reminiscence about *Jim* Smiley. **2.** He's fat and baldheaded with a gentle and simple expression; the narrator finds him by the stove in a run-down tavern in the decayed mining camp of Angel's Camp. **3.** He takes the story very seriously, and tells it in a tone of voice that doesn't vary from start to finish. **4.** He will bet on anything. **5.** that the parson's wife won't recover from her illness **6.** During most of the race she'd be behind, but then she'd get excited, kick up her legs, and coughing, sneezing, and "raising m-o-r-e racket," she'd win by a neck. **7.** In a fight, he'd hang on to the other dog's hind leg until he won the match, but one day he fought a dog that had no hind legs, so he lost the match.

8. an education **9.** He is modest and straightforward. **10.** He fills the frog full of quail shot so that it can't jump. **11.** He begins telling a story about a cow without a tail; the narrator does not want to hear it. **12.** Students' responses may vary in answering whether or not Smiley deserved to be tricked.

Page 94 To Be a Steamboatman

1. to become a steamboatman on the Mississippi River **2.** It is quiet, lazy, and drowsy: "dead and empty." **3.** The town awakens, becomes noisy, bustling, alive with activity. **4.** These phrases should be checked: gorgeous paddle boxes, a glass and gingerbread pilot house, a big bell, a fenced and ornamented texas deck, a gangplank over the port bow, two tall chimneys puffing black smoke **5.** He finds a rusty bolt to polish where everyone can see him; he comes to town wearing his blackest clothes; he uses nautical terms to refer to everything, even a horse; he talks about "St. Looy" as though he lives there, etc. **6.** His steamboat blows up, and he returns to town a battered and bandaged hero. **7.** Everyone left as soon as they could to find jobs on the river. **8.** No, he gets the cold shoulder from everyone. **9.** Answers will vary as students describe some deeply held ambition and the things they have done to achieve it.

Page 95 Shenandoah

1. the Missouri **2.** an Indian camp **3.** "Away you rolling river"; "Ah-ha, I'm bound away 'cross the wide Missouri" **4.** the white man who is in love with Shenandoah's daughter **5.** take Shenandoah's daughter away **6.** money **7.** Shenandoah "disdains" the trader's money and tells the trader he will never have his daughter. **8.** a Yankee skipper **9.** Shenandoah's daughter; she is mourning for her father and her home, having been stolen away by the skipper. **10.** In the first six stanzas, *bound* is used by the traveler who is on his way, or going, across the river. When the Indian maiden speaks of being bound, it means she is restrained and held against her will. **11.** Answers may vary. Dialogue is used both to develop the plot and to create the characters of the Indian chief, his daughter, and those who want to take her away.

Page 96 El Corrido de Gregorio Cortez

1. The Major Sheriff has been killed in El Carmen county. **2.** Gregorio Cortez **3.** bloodhounds
4. Catching Cortez was like following a star.
5. They want the thousand-dollar reward.
6. More than three hundred chase him; even so, he manages to jump out of their trap. **7.** Answers may vary: Perhaps he admires Cortez; perhaps he is ashamed to have so many rangers after him; perhaps he's afraid of making Cortez a martyr, etc.
8. He says he isn't going to put his weapon down until they put him in a cell. **9.** "Ah, so many mounted Rangers/Just to take one Mexican!"
10. He is outnumbered three hundred to one.
11. The hero is an underdog who defends himself against all odds. The poem's author is unknown. It uses dialogue.

Page 97 My Heart Feels Like Bursting and I Will Fight No More Forever

My Heart Feels Like Bursting

1. He loves it. **2.** They speak good things, but they never do what they say. **3.** He wants his people to be raised with Indian ways, not in churches and schools where they will learn only white people's ways. **4.** He loves to roam over the prairies; he doesn't want to settle in one place because when he and his people do, they grow pale and die. **5.** soldiers cutting his timber and killing his buffalo **6.** Students' responses will vary in describing their feelings.

I Will Fight No More Forever

1. Many are dead; others have run away to the hills without food or blankets. **2.** He cares very deeply about their well-being and feels an obligation to do what is best for them. He is heartsick at their plight. **3.** He is exhausted and beaten, in a state of despair about his tribe's future, sad at the death of those in his tribe, and sad at the state his tribe is in.

Page 98 The Outcasts of Poker Flat

1. its "moral atmosphere" **2.** He is neat, seemingly calm and unconcerned, and he may have done something to rouse the townspeople against him.
3. For: He had won money from them and hanging him would be a way of getting it back. Against: they had won money from him and hanging him would be too severe a punishment. **4.** the Duchess, Mother Shipton, and Uncle Billy **5.** They have neither the provisions nor the equipment to set up camp. **6.** Oakhurst had returned the gambling money he won from Tom saying, "Don't try it over again." **7.** No, he tries to talk them out of it. **8.** Uncle Billy **9.** He fears they have been drinking whiskey, but they are just having some "square fun." **10.** the Iliad; "Ash-heels" is Achilles **11.** Mother Shipton, saving her food for the others, dies of starvation; The Duchess and Piney die of exposure. **12.** Answers may vary along the lines that Mr. Oakhurst feels that his life has run its course and that with nowhere to go and no honor left to his name, it is better to kill himself.

Page 99 An Occurrence at Owl Creek Bridge

1. A man, with hands tied behind his back and a rope around his neck, is going to be hanged from a railroad bridge in northern Alabama by soldiers of the Federal (Union) army. **2.** He is thirty-five, well-dressed and with good features, and has a calm demeanor that is unusual in one about to be hanged: He is a gentleman. **3.** A plank spans three crossties on the bridge. A sergeant stands on one end, the condemned man on the other. The sergeant will move aside, the board will tilt, and the man will fall between the ties, hanging by the rope around his neck. **4.** He is a Union soldier.
5. The rope around Farquhar's neck breaks and he falls into the stream. **6.** Following are some of the examples students may include: Sight: saw individual trees, leaves and veins in each leaf; saw the insects on the leaves—spiders, locusts, flies; saw the

colors in the dewdrops on millions of blades of grass; saw the world wheel around; saw the soldiers' gigantic and grotesque shapes; saw the distorted eye of the marksman; etc. Sound: expelled air in a shriek; heard the sounds of the ripples as they touched his face; heard the humming of the gnats, beating of the dragonflies' wings, the strokes of the water-spiders' legs; heard the rush of a fish's body parting the water; heard the soldiers shout; heard the bullet hit the water's surface; etc. Feeling: his neck ached; his heart gave a great leap; body racked and wrenched; felt his head emerge from the stream; eyes were blinded by sun; felt chest expand convulsively; felt ripples of water on his face; felt the visible world pivot around; felt the bullet smack the water; felt his face spattered with spray from the bullet, etc. **7.** The rope around his neck has choked him and he has died.

Page 100 A New England Nun

1. The mood is one of peacefulness, quiet, gentleness, a waning time of life. **2.** Students may pick any of Louisa's actions or mannerisms—how she puts away her sewing things, how she picks and stems currents, how she prepares and eats her tea—and write a description of what those actions reveal about Louisa's character—that she is tidy, meticulous, genteel, etc. **3.** They are both uncomfortable with each other: Louisa feels that Joe is an intrusion into the order and peacefulness of her days, that receiving him is a duty; and Joe doesn't understand Louisa's finickiness and feels like an intruder in her home, though he too goes out of a sense of duty. **4.** It symbolizes her need to erase his presence, to eliminate him from her sphere. **5.** She became accustomed to a solitary life, living quietly and calmly, with no room for another person (or words to that effect). **6.** She will miss distilling essences in her still and sewing linen just for the sake of sewing. **7.** Caesar, like Louisa, is confined to a small world in which he seems reasonably content; like Louisa, there are many things in the world that he will never know. Unlike Louisa, he is paying for a wild rampage in his youth with his confinement, whereas Louisa chooses her life and is not chained to it as Caesar is. **8.** They both refuse to violate the commitment that each feels Joe has made to Louisa: Joe won't go against his word to Louisa; if he did, Lily wouldn't "have" him anyway. They are both honest, principled people who will only do what they perceive to be right.
9. Students' answers may vary; Louisa will probably continue to be happy doing what she has done all along. "Serenity and placid narrowness had become to her as the birthright . . . ."

Page 101 A Pair of Silk Stockings

1. She has unexpectedly come across the large sum of fifteen dollars and she is thinking about the best way to spend it. **2.** She decides to buy shoes, cloth to make clothing, and hats and stockings for her children. **3.** No, she has no time. **4.** She feels faint because she did not eat lunch, so she sits down to recover her "strength and courage."
5. She isn't thinking at all; she is "taking a rest" from thinking and is following "some mechanical impulse." **6.** He can't figure out how someone who looks poor can be wearing silk stockings and acting so particular, as if she weren't poor at all.
7. She buys gloves and magazines, goes to a luxurious restaurant, tips the waiter well, then goes to a movie. **8.** She has had such a pleasant, self-indulgent day that she doesn't want it to end. When the car reaches her stop, she knows she must get off to face the same frustrations and responsibilities that this one day temporarily freed her from.
9. Students' answers will vary.

Page 102 Of the Meaning of Progress

1. in rural Tennessee in the summertime **2.** Josie longs to learn. She seems willing to devote herself to making life "broader, deeper, and fuller." She is energetic, faithful, and has an "unconscious moral heroism." **3.** It is a log hut without a door and chinks between the logs for windows. There is a pale blackboard, a teacher's desk made of three boards, and a single chair that has to be returned each night. The children sit on rough plank benches without backs. **4.** She wants to study at the big school in Nashville, Tennessee; she has a "longing to know." **5.** Josie: longing for knowledge; Martha: brown and dull; Fanny: smooth black face and wondering eyes; 'Thenie: jolly, ugly, good-hearted, dips snuff, looks after her brother; 'Tildy: midnight beauty with starry eyes and tapering limbs; Ruben's girl: chubby, golden face and old-gold hair, solemn and faithful **6.** The Eddings family needs the boys to help with the crops and the girl to mind the baby. The Lawrences doubt the value of book-learning. **7.** Josie's family
8. Those who had experienced slavery were fatalists. Those for whom slavery was a dim memory found the world puzzling—the world asked little, they answered with little, and the world ridiculed the offering. Those who had never known slavery beat against the barriers of caste, youth, and life.
9. Josie: died of exhaustion; Martha: married; Jim: jailed for throwing stones at a man who accused him of stealing; Ben: now farming in Smith County and doing well; 'Tildy: her brother took care of her until she married her lover; Ella (Ruben's girl): now farms and has plenty of babies **10.** Answers will vary.

Page 103 An Episode of War

1. He is measuring out piles of coffee for each squad. **2.** He is shot in the arm. **3.** They all cry out; then they turn and stare at the wood where the shots came from. The lieutenant tries to sheathe his sword, which he now holds in his other hand, by the blade. The men then crowd forward to help him. **4.** They treat him with sympathy, gentleness, and awe; they act as though he has acquired a "terrible majesty," as though if they touched him too hard, he might be sent "headlong" into the unknown, and as though he is closer to the "revelations" of all existence. **5.** Students' answers will vary: he might be in shock, he might not want to take people away from what they are doing, he might feel that he is capable of finding the field hospital by himself. **6.** He sees things happening in the battle that he hadn't been aware of while fighting. **7.** He makes him feel as though he is being scolded because he does not know how to be correctly wounded. **8.** Two ambulances loaded with wounded men have locked wheels, and the drivers argue about who is to blame. Bandaged men come and go, while others sit nursing their wounds. There is another argument raging on the steps of the schoolhouse. A man sits under a tree smoking a pipe. **9.** He wants to rush forward and tell the man smoking the pipe that he is dying. **10.** The surgeon treats him with impatience rather than the respect his fellow soldiers had shown him. The surgeon sees the lieutenant as just one more bothersome man to fix up, while the men had sympathized with the lieutenant. **11.** Answers will vary. Some may see it as simply accepting reality; others may see it as denial or bravado.

Page 104 I Met a Seer, A Man Said to the Universe, and The Wayfarer

I Met a Seer

1. A seer is someone with great wisdom or insight, or someone who can see into the future. The seer holds the book of wisdom in his hands. **2.** to read the book in the seer's hands himself **3.** because the speaker has challenged him when he says he already knows a lot of what is in the book **4.** arrogant, brash, not as wise or smart as he thinks he is **5.** The things in the book—wisdom—are so much greater than the speaker can comprehend that he is blinded by them.

A Man Said to the Universe

1. "I exist!" **2.** Answers may vary, but may include that the universe is indifferent and uncaring, and that one man's existence has no special meaning

The Wayfarer

1. astonishment **2.** that because it is overgrown, it hasn't been traveled in a long time **3.** It is grown over with weeds, and each weed is a knife. **4.** The path is too hard and he thinks there must be an easier way. **5.** Answers will vary. Someone who lacks perseverance or who is arrogant about his abilities until confronted with the realities of a situation.

Page 105 Sympathy

1. the image of the outdoors, which represents freedom **2.** a mood of calm, beauty, and openness; the caged bird creates a twist of yearning, or unhappiness, because the bird can't be free to enjoy this beauty **3.** sun/upland; wind/stirs/springing; first/bird **4.** In the first stanza, the images are of the natural beauty of the outdoors; in the second, they are of the ugliness and brutality of imprisonment. **5.** blood/red **6.** The bird has been beating on the bars of its cage for a long time, and the old scars from those earlier efforts keep on throbbing. **7.** that his song is joyful, when it is actually a prayer, a plea for release **8.** bruised/bosom/beats/bars **9.** The caged bird represents the plight of people who are imprisoned by society's injustices, particularly by the oppression of racism. **10.** because it is a poem that expresses sympathy for and an understanding of the plight of those who are denied freedom

Page 106 Miniver Cheevy and Richard Cory

Miniver Cheevy

1. that he is a "child of scorn," that he is sorry he was ever born, and that he had good reasons to be **2.** the olden times of swords, steeds, and bold warriors **3.** Thebes and Camelot; they represent romance, nobility, and greatness (or words to that effect) **4.** the commonplace **5.** He drinks and blames his life on fate.

Richard Cory

1. well-dressed, well-groomed, slim, and regal in his bearing **2.** He was a gentleman, "human when he talked," who said "good morning" to people. **3.** Everyone watched him; he fluttered pulses when he spoke. **4.** Richard Cory is "imperially slim," he "glittered when he walked," and was "admirably schooled." (The townspeople are "people on the pavement" who work and curse their meager portions.) **5.** Richard Cory killed himself. Answers will vary, but may note that for Cory it was not a calm night at all—it was the (probably) agonizing night he decided to end his life.

Page 107 Lucinda Matlock and Richard Bone

Lucinda Matlock

1. dancing and playing snap-out **2.** Eight of her twelve children died before she was sixty. **3.** She rambled over the fields and by the river gathering shells, flowers, and weeds. She shouted and sang to the hills and woods. **4.** At ninety-six, she had lived long enough and was ready to die. **5.** She grows angry thinking about people—"degenerate sons and daughters," she calls them—who complain about life. Students' answers may vary for the second part of the question; perhaps she is upset seeing people waste life when she made such good use of it.

Richard Bone

1. He carves tombstones. **2.** He did not know whether the epitaphs ("He was so kind," etc.) were really true about the people they were carved for. **3.** He learns which of the epitaphs he chisels are true and which are false. **4.** Answers will vary. Some may describe him as cynical; others as practical. Most will observe that he saw how people really are, without illusions, and yet took money to tell the lies people wanted told about the dead.

Page 108 Mrs. Charles Bliss

1. Each one is advised to stay together "for the sake of the children." **2.** Mrs. Bliss is advised by Reverend Wiley, and Mr. Bliss is advised by Judge Somers. **3.** They are divided in their feelings; two of them side with their mother, and two side with their father. **4.** a mood of disharmony, unhappiness, and divisiveness; of a relentless back and forth movement between two arguing sides **5.** The children felt guilty because they judged harshly the other parent, and were unhappy because they could not admire both parents equally. **6.** to gardeners trying to grow plants without light and in the cold, and to a mother suckling a child on diseased milk **7.** She thinks the advice was terrible, resulting in souls that have experienced only twilight and cold. **8.** She has contempt for the men who gave the advice. **9.** Answers will vary as students give Mrs. Bliss their advice.

Unit 5 The Modern Temper

Page 109 A Wagner Matinée

1. He remembers playing scales on her parlor organ (with hands cracked and sore from cornhusking) while his aunt made canvas mittens. **2.** Red Willow County, Nebraska **3.** She helped him with his Latin, and listened to him reading Shakespeare. She taught him to play the organ. **4.** to the Symphony Orchestra to hear a program of Wagner's music **5.** No, she sits in stony aloofness. **6.** musicians: clean profiles; linen: gloss; coats: dull black; instruments: beloved shapes; fiddle necks and bows: restless, wind-tossed forest **7.** She clutches the narrator's coat sleeve. **8.** They drive downward "like the pelting streaks of rain in a summer shower." **9.** Her fingers "work mechanically" on her lap, as if she were playing the music herself; when the tenor starts to sing, Aunt Georgiana shuts her eyes and tears stream down her cheeks. **10.** He was a young German who had sung at Bayreuth and who could sing the "Prize Song"; to Georgiana, his voice was a reminder of the music she loved but hadn't heard in many years. **11.** "I don't want to go, Clark, I don't want to go." **12.** Answers will vary. Some students, responding to the anguish in Georgiana's last remark, may believe that she will stay in Boston to live the kind of life that has such meaning for her. Others, observing that Georgiana is a woman who takes her responsibilities very seriously, will believe that she will return home to fulfill them.

Page 111 Sophistication

1. the Winesburg County Fair **2.** Crowds fill the stores and sidewalks, horses whinny, clerks rush madly about, children get lost and cry. **3.** George Willard; he is standing in the stairway leading to Doctor Reefy's office, watching the people and waiting for someone **4.** He plans to go to some city and find work on a newspaper. **5.** His mother has died. **6.** when he first looks backward at life (and ghosts whisper a message about life's limitations) **7.** It is the moment a boy, having once been sure of himself, becomes unsure. He sees himself as "a leaf blown by the wind," and realizes how uncertain life is and is acutely aware that death awaits him. **8.** He wants to be close to someone, preferably a woman who will be gentle and understanding; he thinks of Helen White, the banker's daughter. **9.** that he now knows something about manhood that he hadn't known before; that he has changed **10.** She is with a young instructor from her college, thinking about George Willard. **11.** They both feel that they have changed—grown up—and they both want to share their changes with each other. **12.** She has gone away to college, attending the theater and being in crowds, and now feels herself to be more mature. **13.** It describes an evening the two spent together walking along a country road; it serves the purpose of discussing the relationship between the two main characters. **14.** He feels ashamed at the "figure he had made of himself," feeling, probably, that he had boasted too much about becoming an important man. **15.** A band plays, small boys race between men's legs, young men walk with girls, fiddlers tune their instruments, and horns blare. The sounds get on his nerves; he feels closed in. **16.** He trips over a pile of rubbish and tears his trousers, which he mends with a pin. **17.** She is on the veranda of her house with the instructor and her mother. She is restless, distraught, tired of the man's heavy, pompous voice. She runs into the yard and out into a side street. George walks up to her. **18.** the ghosts of the living **19.** because he is with Helen **20.** They laugh and start to pull at each other and run around; Helen trips George and he rolls down the hill. **21.** Answers will vary and should include the use of dialogue.

Page 113 The Jilting of Granny Weatherall

1. The setting is the sickroom of the main character, eighty-year-old Granny Weatherall, who is being attended by Doctor Harry. **2.** "I'd have you respect your elders, young man." Granny Weatherall; ". . . you're going to be good and sorry." Doctor Harry; "The brat ought to be in knee breeches." Granny Weatherall; "We'll have you up in no time." Doctor Harry; "I'll call for you when I want you." Granny Weatherall **3.** "I pay my own bills, and I don't throw my money away on nonsense!" **4.** There is "a dark curtain drawn around the bed"; "the pillow rose and floated under her, pleasant as a hammock in a light wind"; she hears "leaves rustling outside the window" and "swishing newspapers" (which she finally realizes is Cornelia and Doctor Harry whispering together). **5.** She "whispers around doors," keeping "things secret in such a public way," and is overly tactful and kind, and so dutiful that Granny Weatherwall wants to spank her. **6.** The comparison is to a sheet or bedspread, which can be "spread out . . . and tucked in orderly." **7.** as clammy and unfamiliar **8.** In her sixties, she had thought that she was going to die. She visited her children, made a will, and came down with a fever; after that, she stopped worrying about death. **9.** He had died when he was younger than her children are now, and she no longer looks like the woman he married. **10.** She remembers taking care of her children; fencing in one hundred acres; riding country roads in the winter; nursing sick animals and people; and lighting the lamps. **11.** She remembers being jilted on her wedding day. **12.** sixty years **13.** Perhaps the shot feels like an ant biting. **14.** going back through many rooms **15.** She wants to tell him she has forgotten him, and that she had a husband, children, and a house, despite him. George is the man who jilted her. **16.** Answers may vary, either Father Connolly or John. **17.** She wants God to punish George for jilting her, feeling, perhaps, He will punish George the most severely. **18.** to a cart bumping along a bad road; it crashes **19.** She stretches herself and blows out the light. **20.** All answers describing Granny Weatherall from Cornelia's perspective are valid.

Page 115 Winter Dreams

1. He caddies only for pocket money, while many of the others have to work because they are poor. **2.** He owns the second best grocery store in Black Bear. **3.** He wins a golfing match with Mr. T.A. Hedrick; he arrives in a Pierce-Arrow automobile at the Sherry Island Golf Club; he gives an "exhibition of fancy diving." **4.** He says he is too old to caddy. **5.** The flashback describes Dexter Green's meeting with Miss Jones, a rich, spoiled beauty, along with revealing a hasty pride in Dexter Green's nature. It explains why he has suddenly quit caddying. **6.** He quits because Miss Jones calls him "Boy!" and his boss orders him to caddy for her. Rather than do that, he quits on the spot. **7.** to pass up a chance at a business course that his father would have paid for in favor of going to an Eastern college where he feels strapped for money **8.** He buys a partnership in a laundry and makes a specialty of washing woolen golf stockings that well-to-do golfers wear, until he is running a string of five laundries. **9.** He meets her when he is golfing at the club with several others, and her ball goes astray, hitting one of his party in the abdomen. **10.** She is very self-involved, and doesn't seem to care that she has hit Mr. Hedrick. She tells her partner that she would have "gone on the green" with her ball, except that she hit "something." Her "quick insincere smile" and careless "Thank you!" reveals that there is some malice to her selfishness. No, she has not changed at all since she was eleven. **11.** He dislikes her. He thinks she needs to be disciplined and held in check; that she is a flirt, turning her "calf eyes" on all young men in town; that she has no "form." **12.** It is a mood of "intense appreciation." He feels attuned to the beauty and radiance of life. **13.** because he said that she is his ideal **14.** confidence **15.** She has discovered that a man she "cared about" is poor. **16.** "Last night I thought I was in love with a man and tonight I think I'm in love with you—" **17.** that she dates every new man that comes to town and puts everyone else on hold; when her lovers wander away discouraged, she grants them a "brief honeyed hour" to encourage them to "tag along" longer **18.** He asks Irene Scheerer to marry him. **19.** He meets Judy; they ride in his car; she proposes that they marry. **20.** He is indifferent to their opinions; he loves Judy Jones, and having her for only one month is worth it to him. **21.** Judy has married someone who treats her badly, and her beauty has faded away. **22.** Answers will vary. He may be crying because he can't go back to the time when he could care so strongly about someone; or he may have finally realized that he had wasted his life persuing a shallow, ephemeral dream.

Page 117 In Another Country

1. game hanging outside shops, "stiff and heavy and empty," their fur powdered with snow and a cold wind blowing their tails and turning their feathers **2.** He buys roasted chestnuts from a woman, and they stay warm in his pocket. **3.** They are undergoing physical therapy on machines, for wounds they had sustained in the war. **4.** The narrator's knee doesn't bend; the major has a withered hand. **5.** The narrator played football, and the major was the greatest fencer in Italy. **6.** He has no confidence that his hand will be good again. **7.** The people in the communist quarter shouted, "Down with the officers!" **8.** because he wasn't in the war long enough to get one—he was wounded within an hour of arriving at the front **9.** They are all "a little detached." **10.** only their therapy at the hospital and the fact that when they walk through the quarter they feel bound by something the people who don't like them can't understand **11.** because he was an American **12.** They had done heroic things to get their medals. **13.** He knows that he is afraid to die, and that he "would never have done such things." **14.** They were like hunting hawks and he was not. **15.** The men drift apart, although the narrator remains friends with the boy who was wounded his first hour at the front. **16.** the study of Italian grammar **17.** Before he starts studying grammar, Italian seems very easy to him; after he starts studying grammar, he thinks Italian is a very difficult language, and he is afraid to speak to the major. **18.** He says that a person "should not place himself in a position to lose"; that "he should find things that he cannot lose." **19.** because he has just lost his own wife, who suddenly died of pneumonia, and he is "utterly unable to resign himself" **20.** Answers will vary, but should observe that the mood is one of bleak isolation and alienation. Days are cold; lifeless animals hang "heavy and empty." The men return to the hospital each day to repeat a seemingly useless mechanical activity in which they have no faith.

Page 119 The Bear

1. It is about an old, tremendous bear that carries off livestock, escapes traps, mangles dogs, and escapes bullets. **2.** His father, Major de Spain, General Compson, and others would camp in the wilderness and hunt. **3.** Like the wilderness, the bear is "indomitable and invincible," from "an old dead time," the epitome of "the old wild life at which the puny humans swarmed and hacked." Like the wilderness, too, the bear is "doomed." **4.** He refers to the fact that each year, the bear displays again a kind of immortality—the men, their dogs, and their guns, cannot destroy the animal (nor do they seem to want to). **5.** ten **6.** They yap "an octave too high," with a tone of "indecision and even abjectiveness." The sound echoes "thin, slightly hysterical, almost grieving" **7.** Old Ben **8.** to see who's in camp, to see if anyone will be able to shoot him, or if they've found the dog that can "bay and hold him" **9.** He says that, like people, the dog put off being brave for as long as she could, knowing that the

time would come when she would have to be brave "to keep on living with herself," also knowing all along the pain she would suffer because of it.
10. He realizes that the bear, the object of legend and dreams, is also real and can be killed, even though no one has yet had the chance to do it.
11. by the right dog or by accidentally coming upon someone ready to shoot **12.** It is a warm relationship. Sam Fathers teaches the boy about the wilderness, passing on the lore of the bear to him, and shows him how to hunt the bear properly.
13. The boy stands in the spot where Sam Fathers has set him, holding a gun and waiting. He never sees the bear, yet knows it is there, "looking at him." **14.** his gun, watch, compass, and stick
15. The boy leaves camp at sunrise and walks into the wilderness for nine hours. He sits on a log and waits for the bear, which emerges from the wilderness, crosses the glade in which the boy sits, and fades into the deep woods. **16.** He compares the bear to an old bass that sinks back into the "dark depths" of a pool without any movement of its fins. **17.** He has killed a buck and a bear, become a better woodsman than most grown men, can read the trails of all the bears, and can find Old Ben's footprints any time he wants to. **18.** It is a small mongrel, possessed of a kind of bravery that makes it foolhardy. **19.** He throws his gun away, rushes after the dog, and grabs it. **20.** He reads from a poem by Keats, and talks to his son about truth.
21. the bear: fierce, ruthless, with the pride of liberty and freedom, putting liberty and freedom in jeopardy to "savor" them; the old man: Sam Fathers, son of a slave and an Indian, who has learned humility through suffering, and pride through enduring that suffering; the boy: wants to learn humility and pride so that he can know the woods, but grows too skillful too quickly, and who learns about bravery from the old man and the dog; the dog: a mongrel dog that is brave because he has nothing else to offer **22.** Answers will vary, but should reflect Faulkner's symbolizing the bear as all that is deep and abiding in nature.

Page 121 The Leader of the People

1. Billy Buck is raking the old haystack and pitching hay to the cows. Jody is eating bread and butter, scuffing his shoes, throwing stones, and watching Billy. **2.** They are arrogant, smug, and overbearing due to their secure position in the protective hay. **3.** that he likes to give permission for anything that's done on the ranch **4.** Jody: He's excited because he likes his grandfather's stories about Indians and crossing the plains; Mrs. Tiflin: She's angry that her husband is impatient with her father's stories; Carl Tiflin: He's irritated and tired of his father-in-law's repititious stories about a time that has passed. **5.** She says that the crossing was "the biggest thing" in her father's life, and that he would have kept going if the ocean hadn't been there. **6.** Answers may include: The sage has tender new tips; the dogs yap into the brush after rabbits; a crow congress convenes in an oak tree; the wind sings on the hilltops; puffball clouds hurry by. The mood is one of ease and anticipation, matching Jody's excitement about his grandfather's arrival. **7.** He is dressed in black and wears a tie. He carries a black hat. He has a short white beard, white overhanging eyebrows, and blue eyes that are both stern and merry. He is a man of dignity, neat and deliberate, but also good-humored. **8.** to go on a mouse hunt with him **9.** Riley, the boar, ate a hole in the haystack and it fell down and smothered him. **10.** He interrupts Grandfather and tells him that everyone else is ready for dessert; next he tells Grandfather that he has already heard a story "lots of times." **11.** She gets very angry. **12.** He knows just how his grandfather feels, "his insides collapsed and empty." He asks him to tell about the Indians. **13.** He thinks about the world of Indians and buffaloes and about his grandfather taking the people across the plains. He wishes that he could be living in heroic times, but he knows that he is not the heroic sort.
14. He's ready to go out and kill the mice with his grandfather. **15.** When Jody says that the mice don't know what's going to happen to them today, Billy Buck points out that neither does Jody, or himself, or anyone else. **16.** He is being sarcastic.
17. He says that he doesn't mind what Carl has said, but that he would mind if it were true and people really didn't want to hear his stories.
18. how important it was to bring life west, and how the mass of people created a momentum than was beyond any individual **19.** Answers describing how Carl is a man who fits his time, who is content with his lot, and who has no interest in breaking boundaries, are fine.

Page 123 The Man Who Saw the Flood

1. a black father, mother, and child **2.** They are returning home after a flood. **3.** The henhouse and pigpen are gone, the chickens have probably drowned, the road is gone as well as a neighbor's house, the steps to the porch are gone, and the inside of the cabin and the bed are caked with mud.
4. He says that it is like "a mute warning."
5. Their well still pumps clear water; the stove is still usable; they find the ax and some spoons.
6. Burgess is a white man to whom Tom owes money. Tom is reluctant to go to him because he already owes Burgess eight hundred dollars. The cost of setting up the farm will put Tom in deeper bondage to Burgess. **7.** They will be caught and thrown into jail. **8.** matches and tobacco **9.** She doesn't like it, but with Sally and their cow both going hungry, she can't see any other alternative.
10. "You ate that grub, and I got to pay for it, Tom," says Burgess. He's not sympathetic to Tom's plight; he has Tom right where he wants him, and Tom, who needs to feed his family, has no choice but to do what Burgess wants him to do.
11. Because he knows that he is going to be paying back that loan with cheap labor, just as he always does, only now he's going to be deeper in debt than ever before.

Page 124 A Worn Path

1. She is an old, small, black woman carrying a cane made from an umbrella and wearing shoes with the laces untied. She wears a dark striped dress with an apron made of sugar sacks and has a red rag tied around her head; her eyes are so old they are blue and her face is wrinkled "as though a whole little tree stood in the middle of her forehead." **2.** path runs up a hill: "Seems like there is chains about my feet, time I get this far"; caught in thorns: "Thorns, you doing your appointed work" or "I in the thorny bush"; log laid across the creek: "Now comes the trial" or "I wasn't as old as I thought"; buzzard: "Who you watching?" scarecrow: "You scarecrow. I ought to be shut up for good." **3.** She imagines that a little boy offers her a slice of marble cake, and she imagines that the scarecrow is a ghost. **4.** "like old women under a spell sitting there" **5.** "like a little puff of milkweed" **6.** She turns his attention to the black dog, which he then chases away. **7.** She asks the woman to stop and tie her shoes, because it wouldn't look right to go into a building with them untied. **8.** to a clinic in Natchez to get medicine that will soothe the throat of her sick grandson **9.** He swallowed lye several years back, which corroded his throat; now his throat closes up so that he can't swallow or get his breath. **10.** She is going to buy a paper windmill for her grandson. **11.** Descriptions of Phoenix Jackson's homecoming will vary.

Page 125 The Garden

1. She is compared to "a skein of loose silk blown against a wall." **2.** in a public garden called Kensington Gardens **3.** bit by bit of the lack of emotional nourishment—" emotional anaemia" **4.** "a rabble of the filthy, sturdy, unkillable infants of the very poor" **5.** She is like silk, delicate and flimsy; they are filthy and sturdy. She is "dying"; they are "unkillable." They will inherit the earth; she is the "end" of the line. **6.** Answers will vary. He seems to perceive her as emotionally detached, without a strong life force, insubstantial and weak, an example of death in life; his comparison to the strong life force of the "unkillable," sturdy, poor children emphasizes her detachment from life. **7.** Answers will vary. He seems to be saying that her good breeding has bred all the life out of her, and she cannot pass anything on to her descendants, unlike the poor rabble, who will "inherit the earth." **8.** that someone will "commit" the "indiscretion" of talking to her **9.** because she is so very bored and alone **10.** Any responses that retell the poem from the woman's perspective are fine.

Page 126 The River-Merchant's Wife: A Letter

1. that the narrator was a child during the time she speaks of **2.** "Two small people," a boy and a girl; the girl picks flowers, the boy comes by on stilts playing horse. **3.** They liked each other; they had no "dislike or suspicion" of each other. **4.** They get married. **5.** In stanza 2, she is shy and bashful and doesn't smile; in stanza 3, she is a year older and has fallen in love, "desiring her dust to be mingled" with her husband's "forever . . . ." **6.** The husband has gone away and has been gone for five months. **7.** The mood is one of sadness at being parted; the images of monkeys making sad sounds, of the husband dragging his feet as he departs, of the autumn wind bringing the leaves down early establish the mood. **8.** Answers will vary. Time is passing, covering over what was once plainly evident. Her husband's foot no longer tramples the mosses. **9.** The paired butterflies hurt her; she is hurt because they are together at their peak of beauty, while she is separated from her husband and growing older. **10.** She offers to meet her husband at Chō-fū-Sa if he lets her know that he is coming. **11.** Any letter using images to convey emotion written from husband to wife is fine.

Page 127 Patterns

1. walking on a garden path and sitting beneath a lime tree **2.** She is wearing a stiff, brocaded gown richly figured in pink and silver; she has powdered hair and carries a jeweled fan: like everything around her, she is a rare pattern. **3.** Answers may include: the garden paths; the woman's gown and the way the train falls on the gravel; the lime tree's shade, creating patterns of light and shadow; the flowers planted in patterns. **4.** daffodils/squills; gown/down; train/stain; brocade/shade; breeze/please **5.** The contrast is between the rigidness of the patterns and the patterned gown that constrains the woman and the passion that "wars" against those constraints. **6.** The imagery of water, which is loose and freely flowing, makes the woman think of the stroking of her lover's hand. **7.** She would like to take if off; to be free of it and the constraint it represents. **8.** running down the paths, her lover following her, until he catches and embraces her **9.** That the man she was going to marry has been killed in battle. **10.** Answers may vary. It may symbolize her fallen lover or the sorrow she feels at his death. **11.** They were going to be married under the lime tree in a month's time. **12.** She sees herself walking up and down in the garden, winter and summer, still "boned and stayed" in her brocaded gown, now that the one she loved is dead.

Page 128 Chicago

1. hog butchering, tool making, grain storage, railroading, and freight handling **2.** wicked: He has seen painted women luring farm boys; crooked: He has seen gunman kill and go free to kill again; brutal: He has seen women and children go hungry. **3.** He gives them back the sneer; because he believes Chicago is a proud, strong, intelligent city. **4.** a tall bold slugger **5.** flinging curses, amid the toil, piling, job on job, slugger, vivid **6.** "fierce as a dog with tongue lapping . . .," "cunning as a savage pitted against the wilderness . . ." **7.** He conveys the sense of the rugged, hard work with which the city creates the unrelenting, fearless activity of tearing down, building, and rebuilding itself. **8.** the laughter of youth **9.** It is fearless; it doesn't know about failure; it is the laughter of sheer robust health; it is loud, "brawling," proud laughter. **10.** The poem ends by invoking the laughter of the city proud to be Hog Butcher, etc.—and inches back to all the things that Chicago stands for that the poet addressed the poem to in the beginning.

Page 129 Poetry
1. poetry **2.** that there are other things more important **3.** aimless, or fruitless, activity; nonsense **4.** "a place for the genuine" **5.** hands that grasp, eyes that dilate, hair that rises **6.** "we do not admire what we cannot understand" **7.** a bat holding on upside down, elephants pushing, the "immovable critic twitching," the baseball fan, the statistician **8.** They are all "important." **9.** when they are addressed, or "dragged into prominence," by half poets **10.** "literalists of the imagination" **11.** insolence and triviality **12.** "imaginary gardens with real toads in them" **13.** a demand for "the raw material of poetry in all its rawness," and a demand for the "genuine" **14.** Answers will vary. Perhaps what drives them to behave the way they do; perhaps their role in the scheme of things.

Page 130 Spring and All
1. alongside the road to the hospital **2.** contagious **3.** spring; clouds driven by the cold wind; the waste of broad, muddy fields brown with weeds **4.** that they are dead and brown **5.** waste, brown, dried, patches, scattering, forked, twiggy stuff, dead, brown, leafless **6.** lifeless, dazed, sluggish **7.** Students' reasons will vary: *sluggish* may refer to the slow movement of still partially frozen streams or to animals just coming out of hibernation; *dazed* may refer to the effect on animals caused by the full spring sun or the blank, dull look of the landscape. *Lifeless* is only how it appears at first. **8.** only that they enter the world **9.** It is cold, inhospitable, uncertain. **10.** all new life; human life **11.** "stark dignity of entrance" **12.** the beginning of life, birth

Page 131 Ars Poetica
1. palpable and mute **2.** A poem should *be able to be touched* and *felt or experienced* but *not expressed* [or: *silent*]. **3.** It should be dumb. **4.** It should be silent. **5.** It should be wordless. **6.** Answers will vary. Perhaps they are dumb because they cannot speak directly to the person that handles them, but only through the sense of touch. The thumb gathers a feeling of the history and purpose of the medallion. **7.** Answers will again vary. He probably means that the impact of a flight of birds is felt with the senses rather than expressed in words, and that a poem should have the same kind of impact. **8.** It should be motionless in time. **9.** an empty doorway, a maple leaf **10.** leaning grasses, two lights above a sea **11.** its appeal to the emotions or feelings; that its purpose is to simply exist, independent of meaning that might be imposed on it **12.** Answers will vary, but most students will appreciate the irony in analyzing a poem whose main import is that "A poem should not mean/But be."

Page 133 Birches, Fire and Ice, "Out, Out—," Stopping by Woods on a Snowy Evening, Mending Wall
Birches
1. birch trees **2.** the weight of ice after a winter storm **3.** He lives away from town in a place where he has to learn to amuse himself and play alone; he swings on his father's trees as he goes in and out to get the cows; he keeps his poise while climbing the trees and kicks on his way down. **4.** They both swing on trees as boys. **5.** He wishes he could go back and start over again swinging birches; he's afraid that fate might misunderstand his wish and "snatch" him away for good.

Fire and Ice
1. in fire and in ice **2.** He thinks it will end in fire, judging from what he has "tasted" of desire. **3.** He says that he knows enough about hate to know that its coldness would be an equally "great" way to destroy the world. **4.** Fire is desire, ice is hate. **5.** Answers will vary. Possibilities are: fire: anger, loathing, rage, passion, etc. ice: disdain, contempt, disinterest, repulsion, etc.

"Out, Out—"
1. Someone is sawing wood in a yard. It is near sunset, in Vermont, where there are five mountain ranges visible. **2.** The poet writes that the buzz saw *snarled*, and it seems to know the meaning of the word *supper*. It leaps out at the boy's hand and almost seems to attack him. (The use of the active voice gives the buzz saw human qualities.) **3.** not to let the doctor cut his hand off **4.** They, since they are still alive, turn to their own concerns; he wants to say that life goes on around death, and the living are occupied with the business of living.

Stopping by Woods on a Snowy Evening
1. The narrator is riding his horse by a woods, on a snowy evening. He stops to watch the snow fall. **2.** that they have stopped, seemingly without reason, without a farmhouse near **3.** rhyme: know/though/snow; queer/near/year; shake/mistake/flake; sweep/deep/keep/sleep; alliteration: will/watch/woods; farmhouse/frozen; dark/deep; assonance: village/will/fill; farmhouse/darkest; harness/bells; sound/downy; I/miles; consonance: village/will/fill; farmhouse/darkest; his/bells/easy; harness/ask/mistake; sound/downy **4.** a quiet wispy sound full of *s*'s: it is the "easy sweep" of the wind and of the soft flakes of snow falling all around

Mending Wall
1. Frozen ground wells up underneath them, causing boulders to topple from the top and gaps to appear; hunters tear them down looking for rabbits. **2.** No one sees or hears them being made; they seem to appear from nowhere. **3.** an outdoor game, with one person on each side **4.** because his neighbor has pines, and he has an apple orchard, and neither's trees are going to pick up and go anywhere, and neither has cows to trample the other's land **5.** "Good fences make good neighbors." **6.** what he was walling in, what he was walling out, and who he'd be offending by building the wall

Page 135 Theme for English B and November Cotton Flower
Theme for English B
1. His English instructor told his class to go home and write a page and to let the page come out of

each person's self. **2.** Facts may include: He's twenty-two, colored, and was born in Winston-Salem; he has gone to school there, in Durham, and now in Harlem. He is the only black person in his English class. He lives at the Harlem Branch of the Y. **3.** He likes to eat, sleep, drink, and be in love. He likes to work, read, learn, and understand life. For Christmas, he likes to get a pipe or records—blues, jazz, or classical. **4.** Being black "doesn't make me *not* like the same things" people of other races like. **5.** They are each a part of the other, whether or not they want to be; they each learn from the other, whether they want to or not. **6.** Students' responses will vary as they write their own poem "for English B."

November Cotton Flower

1. They look rusty, like they've been around for several seasons. **2.** the boll weevil, the cold winter, and the drought **3.** He says that it is scarce as snow in the South. **4.** The soil was so dry from drought that it sucked all the water from the streams; and birds died and were found below ground in wells. **5.** The cotton flower bloomed. **6.** The flower's blooming gave them love "without a trace of fear" for the beauty that was so rare in the hard conditions they lived in.

Page 136 Any Human to Another and The Creation

Any Human to Another

1. The ills I sorrow at do not pierce only me, through fat and past the bone to the very marrow. **2.** The grief of one mingles with the grief of the others, different yet still together. **3.** No one should think that they can be happy all by themselves, without any concern for the feelings of others. **4.** Joy is shy and friendly to only a few; grief talks to anyone, whether they deserve it or not. **5.** grief: "like a blade shining and unsheathed"; sorrow: "like a crown" of bitter aloes

The Creation

1. He's lonely. **2.** He says that the darkness was "blacker than a hundred midnights down in a cypress swamp." **3.** sun: He gathers up light and rolls it into a ball in his hands, and sets it in the heavens; moon and stars: He takes the light that's left from making the sun and flings it against the darkness; valleys and mountains: He walks over the earth and his footsteps create valleys and mountains; seven seas: He sees that the world is barren, so he spits out the seven seas. **4.** fishes and fowls, beasts and birds **5.** He still feels lonely. **6.** He scoops clay from the riverbed and shapes it into his own image. Then he blows life into it. He is like "a mammy tending over her baby."

Page 137 A Black Man Talks of Reaping and If We Must Die

A Black Man Talks of Reaping

1. that the speaker of the poem has sown seed everywhere **2.** that the wind and birds would steal away the grain that he had planted **3.** "this stark, lean year" **4.** only the harvest he can hold in one hand **5.** scattered/seed; hand/hold **6.** everything that the speaker has sown, "stalk and root" **7.** only what has been left behind by the "brother's sons"; "bitter fruit"

If We Must Die

1. the ignoble, mindless slaughter of the helpless (perhaps for sport) **2.** those who slaughter, harass, and mock **3.** They must fight and die nobly, rather than be penned and die ingloriously **4.** "O kinsmen! We must meet the common foe!" **5.** He points out that they can deliver one mighty killing blow to their enemies and that it is better to die bravely when death is inevitable. **6.** on the image of the "mad and hungry dogs" introduced earlier; it is effective because it illustrates that animals that roam in packs are like a human mob—they rage out of control, mindless and cruel

Page 139 The Love Song of J. Alfred Prufrock

1. It is "like a patient etherised upon a table." **2.** The mood is one of boredom, loneliness, desolation, and emptiness; the words establishing this mood include etherised, half-deserted streets, muttering retreats, restless nights, one-night cheap hotels, tedious argument, insidious intent. **3.** No, they aren't even listening to one another—just talking and moving. **4.** the yellow fog; it represents a cat **5.** It rubs its body on window-panes, licks "its tongue into the corners of the evening," lingers, slips, leaps, wraps itself around the house, and falls asleep. **6.** Students can list any three of the following: time for "the yellow smoke that slides along the street," time to "prepare a face to meet the faces that you meet," time to "murder and create," "time for all the works and days of hands/That lift and drop a question on your plate," time for you and for me, "for a hundred indecisions . . . visions and revisions,/Before . . .toast and tea" **7.** Answers may vary, but he seems to be a procrastinator; he would rather wait for another time to do things; he doesn't want to act right away on anything. **8.** He has a bald spot in the middle of his thinning hair; he wears a coat with a high collar and a "rich and modest" necktie with a simple pin; he is thin. **9.** rhyme: dare/stair/hair; thin/chin/pin; decisions/revisions; universe/reverse; consonance: morning/mounting; bald/middle/will/collar; alliteration: morning/mounting/modest/middle; collar/coat **10.** Students' responses can vary along the following lines: that he has taken no risks; that he has measured out life's experiences in small amounts. **11.** They "fix you with a formulated phrase," and pin you to a wall. **12.** They are braceleted, white, and bare, downed with light brown hair; they lie along a table and wrap around a shawl. **13.** "a pair of ragged claws/Scuttling across the floors of silent seas"; he lives a life so isolated from others that he should have been a hard-shelled crab at the bottom of the sea
14. lines 2 and 3, in which the evening is "spread out" like a patient on a table; and/or the imagery in lines 20-23, in which the fog curls around the house and falls asleep **15.** Answers will surely vary. Perhaps he wants to try and break out of the meaningless, deadening world in which he exists.

16. fear **17.** He wonders if it "would have been worth it." **18.** the image of squeezing the universe into a ball and rolling it toward the question
19. sunsets, dooryards, streets, novels, teacups, skirts, floor, pillow, and shawl **20.** the allusion to Hamlet, the hero in a Shakespearean tragedy
21. He is the attendant lord, the one who helps to build the drama of a scene, but not the lead player—not Hamlet. He is an advisor, a tool, defers to others, is glad to be of use; is a fine speaker but hard to understand, seems almost ridiculous, almost a fool. **22.** a tone of resignation and doubt
23. He no longer thinks that he can do anything to change the way he lives his life; he is resigned to his decline, to fussing about inessentials like where he should part his hair and whether he should eat a peach. **24.** Answers will vary. Where the rest of the poem makes use of details of daily life—coffee spoons, dooryards, restless streets—to build the effect of the mundaneness and dreariness of Prufrock's limited life, the mermaids are fantastic, unreal, and inaccessible—out of Prufrock's limited grasp. Some students may be aware of the allusion to Ulysses and the sirens' song of adventure and sensuality. Prufrock longs to be like Ulysses, brave and true, but knows he will never be.

Page 141 Abraham Lincoln Walks at Midnight and Mountain Woman

Abraham Lincoln Walks at Midnight

1. A mourning figure paces up and down and will not rest. **2.** near the old courthouse, by his old home, in the yards where his children used to play, or through the market **3.** He is thin, dressed in an old black suit, high top hat, and plain shawl—all images associated with Abraham Lincoln.
4. war: "The sins of all the war lords burn his heart." **5.** when the world is at peace and Europe is free **6.** that all his hard work to set people free seems wasted; people learned nothing from it
7. He wonders who will bring peace to the world, or if there is anyone capable of it.

The Mountain Woman

1. The mood is stark and somber; the "sullen" peaks, "life's hard account," the days are a "burden," the winter sky is "somber," and the woman is sharply etched against it. **2.** She's responsible for the well-being of her family; she plows the arid soil, drives the steers, rears her children; her lot in life ages her, stealing youth and hope from her face. **3.** The sheriff shoots her oldest son beside his still. **4.** She does not cry, but stands upright throughout the ordeal. **5.** He destroys a flower that she is tending "with a reverent touch."
6. Students' answers may vary. Perhaps she tended the flower in her son's memory, or for his grave, and losing the flower was like losing him a second time. Perhaps she couldn't bear losing the only beautiful thing in her life.

Page 142 Well, I Have Lost You and Pretty Words

Well, I Have Lost You

1. She has lost someone she cared about, but with her own consent. **2.** She takes full responsibility.
3. that she accepted the outcome of the situation with the same kind of courageous pride overthrown kings have as they go "to their deaths" **4.** The metaphor is of a caged bird, or "wing." She had too much pride to keep anyone "rubbed in a cage" who would rather be free. **5.** She remembers their time together. **6.** She anticipates outliving her anguish and having only good things to say about the person she loved so well.

Pretty Words

1. words as pets **2.** smooth: like gold-enamelled fish; tender: like downy-feathered birds; shy: deep-eyed deer in herds **3.** Words are represented as bright songbirds. **4.** After the simple and elegant comparisons to "pretty, docile" words, the poet ends by saying that she likes words that are like bees: "honied," and "with a little sting." **5.** Students' answers will vary in choosing a metaphor for language and making a list of the things they love about words.

Page 143 Boats in a Fog and The Solitary

Boats in a Fog

1. sports, gallantries, the stage, the arts, dancers, music **2.** bitter earnestness **3.** The poet shifts away from the abstract contemplation of beauty and moves his gaze to the specific details of the ocean and boats on it. **4.** fishing boats returning to their port in a dense fog **5.** The mood is quiet, somber, fraught with danger; words used are mystery, difficult path, peril, trailing, crept, subdued, patient, and cautious. **6.** All three move in a logical, predetermined way. Many find watching their movement fascinating.

The Solitary

1. She has become more self-sufficient, more content in herself. **2.** that she has herself and her will; that she has the strength to enjoy the world around her **3.** The tone is one of seeming detachment and unconcern; students' responses may vary in stating what they have learned about the speaker, who seems ready to deceive those who think she loves them. **4.** Students' responses may vary; the poem is about the speaker's feelings, not the feelings of others. She seems to care enough about others to avoid hurting them but not enough to return their feelings in kind. **5.** Responses will vary in explaining what they think the phrase means; many may mention the jarring combination of a soft, fragrant rose and a cold, hard stone. Whether or not they feel that way is a purely individual matter.

Page 144 Anecdote of the Jar and Janet Waking

Anecdote of the Jar

1. The speaker has placed a jar on a hill in Tennessee. **2.** The jar provides a contrast with the wilderness, dominating and taming it. **3.** The word *slovenly* describes the untidy, uncontrolled, and uncontrollable aspect of nature; it's connotation, a negative one, implies that nature is not as neat and orderly as man's works. **4.** Student responses may vary, along the lines that the jar is made by man and so may symbolize the works of man (art, imagination, industry, etc.), unlike the wilderness. **5.** Students' answers will vary in describing the poet's point of view, taking into account an element of verbal irony in the poem. The wilderness may be slovenly and sprawling, but the jar cannot "give of bird or bush," cannot grow, change, and die.

Janet Waking

1. sleeping **2.** her hen **3.** Her hen, Chucky, has died, stung by a bee. **4.** The bee has changed Chucky in a surprising and grotesque way. Chucky not only looks different but she is, surprisingly, dead. **5.** It is death. It may be thought of as forgetful because the dead have no memory of life. **6.** The poet's tone is matter-of-fact and somewhat ironic.

Page 145 anyone lived in a pretty how town and 1(a

anyone lived in a pretty how town

1. up: down; summer: winter; did: didn't **2.** They dislike anyone. They sow their isn't; they reap the same thing. **3.** Noone loves anyone. **4.** married, laughed, did, sleep, wake, hope, said, slept; someones and everyones **5.** It conveys the sense of passing time. **6.** They die and are buried. **7.** "went their came" **8.** Answers will vary. It's probably a love story: Noone loves anyone. The people in the town think little of either of them. They die and are, perhaps, reunited in heaven.

1(a

1. *a leaf falls* **2.** *loneliness* **3.** Answers may vary. The image of one leaf falling evokes the mood implied in the word *loneliness*. **4.** Answers will vary. The motion of a falling leaf may be seen to be represented by the cascading formation of the letters. The structure also looks like the number "1." **5.** Any response using no more than five words and one image to create the mood the student associates with the word *solitude* is fine.

Page 146 Lament of the Normal Child and Childhood

Lament of the Normal Child

1. "Cherish the Problem Cases!" **2.** This child is normal and all the rest of the children have complexes or hyperactive glands or something that requires special attention. **3.** He describes himself as being a square peg in a square hole. **4.** Frederick Knipe: perfect example of antisocial attitude; Cuthbert Jones: has a textbook case of temper; Jessamine Gray: cheats because she's undernourished; Mortimer Sears: has a Oedipus complex. **5.** He wishes he had a complex of his own, so he could have some attention also.

Childhood

1. They dressed raggedly, wearing carbide lamps, and came down the hills dyed red with the dust from the mines. **2.** *Undermine* means to undercut; at the same time, it refers to the *mining* that the men do, *under* the ground, so the word echoes within the poem. **3.** famine, terror, flood, and plague **4.** hatred **5.** the "sentiment and hatred," bitter feelings

Page 147 University Days

1. He could never see what he was supposed to see through a microscope. **2.** a vague milky substance **3.** He grows enraged at the narrator, quivering all over and accusing him of deliberately not seeing anything. **4.** the reflection of his own eye **5.** Bolenciecwcz; he's a tackle on the football team **6.** "while he was not dumber than an ox he was not any smarter" **7.** The professor asks Bolenciecwcz to name one means of transportation. They imitate the sounds a train makes. **8.** A friend gave the narrator's number, and swam in his place. **9.** He is an agricultural student; he took up journalism to give him something to fall back on if farming doesn't pan out. **10.** Haskins discovers that the horses have sores on them. **11.** While World War I is being fought in Europe, the students at this college are learning military drills that would be of use to someone fighting the Civil War. **12.** With General Littlefield giving drill instructions as quickly as he can, only the narrator succeeds in following all the orders in succession, so that he is marching alone. The narrator is made a corporal for his achievement. **13.** Students' answers will vary.

Page 148 from One Writer's Beginnings

1. She acts as the navigator and she also keeps track of the miles and routes traveled and the trip's expenses. **2.** as if it were an adversary **3.** The two children rode in the back with their legs over suitcases; other suitcases were strapped on the running boards. Whenever it rained too hard to see, they stopped the car, snapped on rain curtains, and played games until the rain stopped. The entire trip took about one week each way. **4.** It had her father by the shoulders and hair. **5.** She has inherited his nervous energy, and just as he couldn't stop when he was in the grip of the road, she can't stop "writing on a story." **6.** "bleached and frazzled as if made from cornshucks" **7.** Her father is an optimist who is always prepared for the worst; her mother is a pessimist who takes all the risks. **8.** During a fire, she ran back into a burning house to rescue her twenty-four volume set of Dickens, which she threw out the window, thereafter jumping out herself. **9.** the water **10.** They have clear identities: identities made up of houses, yards, fields, people busy working, details that you could recognize the next time you went through them, the same way you recognize people you know. **11.** At the beginning, "going through the country" simply describes the method of travel; by the end of the selection, "going through the country" means coming to know it intimately, getting acquainted with the country in the same way you'd get acquainted with someone.

Page 149 Tell Your Children

1. that American Indians are "one hundred percent" American; they are the First Americans

2. They call white victories "battles" and Indian victories "massacres." 3. the Battle of Wounded Knee, where Sioux were killed by federal troops, and the Battle of the Little Big Horn, where federal troops were killed by Sioux 4. They say that Indians were acting in self-defense, defending their lands, hunting grounds, forests, and buffalo, all of which were stolen or killed by white people.
5. White people who defend their property are called patriots; Indians who do the same thing are called murderers. 6. They overlook the treaties they made with Indians that were broken.
7. thieves: Indians lived in a society where locks and bars were not necessary; savages: Indian civilization has all the hallmarks of a civilization: religion and philosophy, arts, music, story and legend.
8. the running of waters, the sighing of winds, and the call of the animals 9. Answers should include some of these: the songs of nature, so that children can learn to love nature as the Indians love it; the oratory of their statesmen; games played for health; the legends and stories of the Indian people; that Indians killed for food, not fun; the history of the friendly acts of the Indians towards early settlers; of Indian heroes and leaders; the history of Indian's part in fighting in the World War. 10. that they fought for a country of which they were not citizens, for a flag they had no claim to, for a people who had treated them unjustly

Unit 6 Modern Drama

Page 151 The Glass Managerie: Act One, Scenes 1, 2, and 3

1. He says that Tom, acting as the narrator, is "an undisguised convention of the play" and that he "takes whatever license with dramatic convention as is convenient to his purposes." 2. A memory play is dimly lighted, sentimental, not realistic, and everything happens to music. 3. He was a telephone man who "fell in love with long distance" and ran out on his family. The last thing his family ever heard of him was a postcard from Mexico with a two-word message: "Hello—Goodbye!" 4. He tells her that he hasn't enjoyed one bite of his dinner and that her constant attention is the reason he hurries through his meals. 5. They were all gentlemen, all prominent planters and sons of planters, and all of them went on to be wealthy. 6. She fears that Laura will be an old maid. 7. She is polishing her glass managerie and listening to a record; when she hears her mother coming, she goes to her typewriter and starts typing. 8. She tells Laura that she didn't have the strength to go, and then she takes Laura's typing charts and tears them up. 9. that Laura has not been attending business college 10. She threw up on the floor and could not return. 11. She describes the lives of "barely tolerated spinsters," tucked away in small rooms and "eating the crust of humility all their lives," shunted from one relative to another. 12. Jim, a cheerful guy who sang in the school operetta, dated a girl Laura found "insincere." Jim seems to have been quite friendly toward Laura, nicknaming her "Blue Roses." 13. She is surprised and says, "I'm—crippled!" 14. Cultivate something to take its place, such as vivacity or charm. 15. narrator of the play 16. She becomes obsessed with the idea of finding a gentleman caller for Laura.
17. It begins when Amanda starts interfering with Tom while he is trying to write—adjusting his lamp, telling him how to sit—and Tom swears at her. 18. He accuses her of leaving him nothing of his own and of confiscating his books. She accuses him of lying about going to the movies every night, saying that no one goes to the movies every night.
19. The one activity Tom doesn't mention is driving a get-away car for a gang of bank robbers.
20. It shatters Laura's glass menagerie. 21. The tone is angry and sarcastic (he doesn't do any of the horrible things he describes to his mother, but he is tired of her harassing him and he mocks her concern about the way he lives his life).

Page 153 The Glass Menagerie: Act One, Scenes 4, 5, and 6

1. Tom is drunk. 2. Malvolio is a magician who does "wonderful tricks," according to Tom. He turns water into whiskey, goldfish into birds and vice versa, and escapes from a nailed coffin. 3. In his opening speech, as narrator, Tom says that he has "tricks in his pocket" and "things up his sleeve," and that he is the opposite of a stage magician. 4. She begs Tom to apologize to their mother for what he said to her the night before.
5. They are hurt and angry with each other; relations between them are strained. 6. that he won't become a drunkard 7. that he likes adventure, and he doesn't get enough adventure where he works 8. She was crying because she thinks Tom is unhappy there. 9. He is a lover, a fighter, and a hunter. 10. She sees it as something that belongs to animals and that people should move away from, something that "Christian adults" don't want any part of. 11. Laura will have to marry someone to take Tom's place. 12. She asks him to find a nice young man for his sister (one who doesn't drink). He says he will. 13. Students' responses may vary, but it seems sad and resigned, alluding to the "change and adventure" imposed on young, unsuspecting kids by war and unrest in Europe. Life in the Paradise Dance Hall seems all the more "brief" and "deceptive" when placed alongside Berchtesgaden and Guernica. 14. He has asked a gentleman caller home for dinner. 15. She becomes upset, saying she hasn't enough time to prepare, that the place is a pigsty, and that they "haven't got it." 16. because the caller's name is O'Conner—she assumes he is Catholic and can't eat meat on Friday (the day of his anticipated visit)
17. He is shipping clerk, making about eighty-five dollars a month. 18. His face "fooled everybody," Amanda says, "all he had to do was grin and the world was bewitched." 19. He is "medium homely"—freckle-faced, with a large nose. 20. He goes to night school. 21. a portrait of someone who is "different" from other girls, someone who is painfully shy, who lives in a world of her own, and who might seem peculiar to people outside of their home 22. Answers will vary. The two women share a dependence on Tom—they need him to act as go-between and to bring news of the real world. Both Amanda and Laura live in a world of their own making—a world many shades removed from realistic. While Laura is shy, restrained, and very

compliant, however, her mother is very dramatic, exuberant, and feisty.

Page 155 The Glass Menagerie: Act Two, Scenes 7 and 8

1. In high school, O'Connor seemed destined for great things, but after graduation, he seemed to hit a snag—he is holding a job not much better than Tom's. **2.** She is nervous and distraught; her mother's fussing over the dinner has made the event seem "so important." **3.** She says they *are* setting a trap, and that men expect it. **4.** She tells about how she collected jonquils everywhere she went with her gentlemen callers; the story tells about Amanda's youth, her single-minded craving for beauty, and about her nostalgia for a period in her life when she was appreciated by everyone and had no cares in life except to make it to the next ball. **5.** She fears that it will be the same Jim that she knew in high school. (If it is, she tells her mother, she will have to be excused from supper.) **6.** She is "stiff and trembling," her hands cold. She leaves the room as soon as she can. **7.** He says that he is at the point of making a change and starting a future that doesn't include the warehouse, their boss, or a course in public speaking. **8.** He says people go to the movies to watch adventures instead of having their own. They come out of the dark room when there is a war. **9.** with the money that was to have paid the electric bill **10.** Like his father, Tom is planning to leave town without telling his family. **11.** At first he is startled by her appearance and her "Southern vivacity," but he soon warms to her and is "won over." **12.** She is taken back to the time when she herself had "gentlemen callers" and, dressed in her finery, is acting very much as she might have when she was young. **13.** She tells him about her gentlemen callers, her expectations of marrying a rich planter, her acceptance of her husband's proposal. She tells him about the "tribulations"of her life now, with all vestiges of gracious living "Gone, gone, gone," and of her husband who "travels" places—she doesn't know where. **14.** The lights go out (shut off by the electric company because Tom hasn't paid the bill). **15.** She tells him he can go into the front room where Laura is "all by her lonesome," and visit with her. **16.** He asks her to sit on the floor, close enough so that he can see her; he offers her gum, and starts talking to her about Chicago and the world's fair he saw there. **17.** To her the clumping of her braces always sounded like thunder; Jim O'Connor "never even noticed" anything noisy about her entrances, other than that she was always late. **18.** She tells him that her braces stood between her and others and she couldn't overcome her feelings and make friends. **19.** He is disappointed that he is not further along than he is, considering how promising everyone thought him in high school. **20.** He decides that she has an inferiority complex, that she lacks confidence in herself. **21.** her glass menagerie **22.** She is calm, and says that maybe it's a blessing in disguise—now he is like all the other horses. **23.** He is engaged to someone named Betty. **24.** He leaves home for good. **25.** Answers may vary. Most will feel it is a symbol of Laura, different from everyone else, fragile and easily broken if handled carelessly, and "extinct in the modern world."

Unit 7 New Frontiers

Page 157 Man and Daughter in the Cold

1. Ethan, his friend Matt Langley, Ethan's daughter Becky, and Ethan's twin sons **2.** disconnecting cold, air like slices of transparent metal, face red with windburn **3.** that she is making conversation with Matt all on her own **4.** He says to Ethan that she doesn't cheat, and tells Becky that she is Olympic material. **5.** a feeling of being "encumbered," crowds or sensations of crowding, delay **6.** He flinches from it and the way his classes eat his life year by year. **7.** "His septum tingled like glass"; "The cold . . . shone through his clothes like furious light"; "The cold had the quality not of absence but of force: an inverted burning." **8.** He suffers an asthma attack and can barely breathe. Becky helps him by waiting for him at intervals and by suggesting the easiest route down. **9.** She tells him that it is like a tree inside him, with branches with rings of muscle that tighten; he likes her lecture. **10.** He refers to the "many-headed immortality of [his students'] annual renewal," the "cruel onward flow" of youth that leaves him behind while devouring his own youth. When Becky skis ahead of her father and waits for him to catch up, he is left behind by her youth and assurance in the adverse climate of the mountain; Ethan sees Becky as part of that pageant that will leave him behind as he grows older and death approaches.

Page 158 The First Seven Years

1. He respects and admires Max for his diligence and sacrifice to go to college; his daughter causes him grief because she refuses to go to college. **2.** Sobel is Feld's helper; he also advises Miriam on reading the classics. **3.** to ask Max if he would like to go out with Miriam **4.** He is "tall and grotesquely thin," sharp featured, with a "beak-like" nose; he dresses in a long, loose overcoat, battered shoes, and an old hat. **5.** Sobel, obviously very angry, grabs his coat and runs out of the shop. Feld has a bad heart and cannot do much, so he relies heavily on Sobel, a man who works for little money and is completely trustworthy. **6.** Responses to the question may vary; she says, "It was all right," but seems unenthuiastic about Max. She does agree to see him again, however. **7.** She decides that he is "nothing more than a materialist," doesn't have a soul, is only interested in things, and is boring. **8.** He's angry because Feld never considered him as a possible husband for Miriam. **9.** that Sobel wait for two years, when Miriam will be twenty-one. **10.** Answers will vary; most students will probably express the opinion that they will marry.

Page 159 The Wooing of Ariadne

1. The story is written from the first person point of view; the narrator is Marko Palamas. **2.** He has

an old-fashioned view of women: Women are to be pursued and to "lend grace to the pursuit"; he sees homely, "banana-bodied" women as an outrage to his sense of self; he thinks that short hair is a "modern aberration" and finds it "revolting."
3. She studies him, nods with "the barest minimum of courtesy," and refuses to dance with him when he asks her. When he presses her, she tells him he resembles a gorilla and his manners are those of a pig. When he tells her that he loves her, she punches him in the eye. **4.** He thinks that her rejection merely shows that she wants him to pursue her more diligently and that her passion for him is as "intense" as his for her. **5.** Marko goes to her father's grocery shop to see Ariadne. When she won't open the door to see him, Marko goes out into the street and begins shouting up at her, telling her that he wants to call on her. She shrieks at him from her window to go away. When he doesn't, she throws crockery and a water pitcher at him. **6.** Father Marlas, Uncle Paul, and Ariadne
7. The mood is tense, strained: Ariadne and her family are ready to fight Marko if he doesn't leave her alone. **8.** They are concerned that Marko is forcing his attentions on Ariadne. **9.** He says that he has acted the only way he knows how—honestly and straightforwardly—that he saw Ariadne and loved her and that he feels no shame over the violence of his emotions for her. **10.** Students responses may vary in answering; she seems to see something in him she had not seen before.

Page 160 The Haunted Boy

1. There is no fire in the grate. The quiet and the chill remind him of something that frightens him, of "the other time." **2.** He is older, the best student in the sophomore class but not a teacher's pet, a good athlete. **3.** He is worried that his mother isn't at home and hasn't left a note for him.
4. that John thinks he is being a sissy for worrying about his mother **5.** that John is being serious and asking him a serious question about his mother
6. Hugh's mother thought she was going to have a baby; instead she had a tumor and had to be operated on; soon after that, his mother attempted suicide. **7.** He asks John to stay and talk a while, starts a game of basketball, offers him more pie, lies about a hi-fi he is assembling, asks him to come upstairs. **8.** When he realizes that his mother is not in the bathroom, bleeding to death, he begins to cry from relief; then he cries because he never cried about his mother before now, and everything comes out at once. **9.** He is angry with her for what she did to him, by attempting suicide and letting him find her. **10.** He tells Hugh that he has been "fine, . . . damn fine" during the hard times when Hugh's mother was in the hospital. Hugh's face burns with pride that his father is addressing him as if he were an adult, and Hugh's terror, anger, and fear all disappear. **11.** Students' responses describing ways in which Hugh's mother might also be considered "haunted" are all valid.

Page 161 Harrison Bergeron

1. Everyone has finally been made equal "every which way." **2.** Everyone goes crazy because it still isn't springtime, and the Handicapper General's men take George and Hazel Bergeron's son, Harrison, away. **3.** Hazel, being of average intelligence, can't think for very long about anything; George, who has above-average intelligence, has a mental handicap radio in his ear that emits sharp noises to prevent him from thinking. **4.** They are weighted down with weights and bags of birdshot, and wear masks, so that no one can feel inferior about their beauty or their gracefulness. **5.** a twenty-one-gun salute **6.** for removing the lead balls from his handicap bag **7.** He is a genius, an athlete, and he is under-handicapped. **8.** **1).** Harrison Bergeron's picture appears on the television screen. **2).** Harrison Bergeron declares that he is the Emperor. **3).** Harrison Bergeron strips off his physical and mental handicaps. **4).** Harrison Bergeron dances with the ballerina. **5).** Diana Moon Glampers, Handicapper General, invades the studio with a shotgun. **9.** George gets up to get a beer and doesn't see the whole thing; Hazel has been crying about having seen something sad on the screen, but she can't quite remember what it was.
10. Students' responses may vary. Vonnegut is satirizing the overriding impulse for conformity in our society and the tendency to overemphasize equality. He pokes fun at those who consider the strive for excellence or brilliance elitist snobbery.

Page 162 The Life You Save May Be Our Own

1. Tom T. Shiftlet: A tramp with one half-arm; he is thin and lists to one side; he has slick black hair parted in the middle and a long narrow face; he wears a black suit and a brown felt hat, and carries a tin tool box. Lucynell Crater (mother): An old woman "the size of a cedar fence post; she wears a man's gray hat pulled down over her head. Lucynell Crater (daughter): A large girl with pink-gold hair and blue eyes; she wears a short blue organdy dress; she is "afflicted" and grows excited when she spies Mr. Shiftlet, making noises and stamping her feet. **2.** She offers him food and a place to sleep in return for work done around the place.
3. as sitting on a fig tree branch, "as if it were going to roost there with the chickens." **4.** The mother is offering Shiftlet her daughter in marriage; he agrees to stay around the place because he really wants the car. **5.** sugarpie **6.** almost thirty
7. She says, "Saturday, you and her and me can drive into town and get married." **8.** He says it was "just something a woman in an office did, nothing but paper work and blood tests"; perhaps it was too impersonal. **9.** He is depressed.
10. He says his mother is a "flea bag" and that Tom Shiftlet's mother is a "stinking polecat."
11. Students' responses will vary, but he probably sees her as an awesome burden, and he is a man incapable of really caring about anyone but himself.

Page 163 Marigolds

1. the dust of late summer **2.** They evoke the "chaotic emotions of adolescence . . . joy and rage and wild animal gladness and shame." **3.** It is more ramshackle than the rest of the ramshackle homes. **4.** When they were little, they thought she was a witch; now that they are older, they still see her as being strange and alien to them. She is very mysterious; they can't figure out how she eats, or whether she eats, or how she manages the "necessities" of life without ever leaving her yard. **5.** They don't understand the marigolds, which were too beautiful for Miss Lottie's ugly place; they "said too much" that the children couldn't understand. **6.** She feels ashamed; the child in her sulks and tells her that it was all in good fun, but the adult in her flinches at the thought of the attack on the old woman. **7.** She is bewildered and frightened at hearing her father cry because he can't support his family. Her father's crying makes him seem a small child, which sets her world askew. **8.** She feels the lack of her mother's attention, the hopelessness of the family's poverty, the bewilderment of being "neither child nor woman," and the fear caused by hearing her father cry. **9.** The narrator sees that Miss Lottie was not a witch but a broken old woman for whom the garden was a small expression of love, beauty, and joy. The narrator now must see what is below the surface and feel compassion, which makes her no longer innocent, thus marking the end of childhood, according to the author.

Page 165 The Secret and The Writer

The Secret

1. Two girls believe they have discovered the secret of life in the line of a poem. **2.** Though she wrote the line, she doesn't know the secret, nor does she know what line the girls are referring to. **3.** She assumes that they have forgotten everything: the secret, the line, even the name of the poem. **4.** They will discover the "secret of life" over and over until they die, and they will find it everywhere ("in other/lines/in other/happenings"). **5.** that they assume that there is a secret to know

The Writer

1. writing a story **2.** "like a chain hauled over a gunwale" **3.** that of a ship; she sits in the prow, her typewriter sounding like "a chain . . . over a gunwale; she carries a "great cargo . . . some of it heavy"; he wishes her a "lucky passage." **4.** He remembers a starling that was trapped in the same room his daughter is writing in. **5.** dazed, wild, dark, batter, drop like a glove, humped and bloody **6.** He sees that they both have to struggle with "life or death," and that even so, it is possible to beat "a smooth course for the right window," to succeed.

Page 166 To David, About His Education and The Vision Test

To David, About His Education

1. It is addressed to David, and it is about his education. **2.** by putting the mind's eye—or nose—into a book **3.** the square root of Everest, how many time Byron goes into Texas, if the law of the excluded middle applies west of the Rockies; the mean annual rainfall on Plato's Republic; and the calorie content of the Diet of Worms; the are all nonsensical, but they sound like the sorts of things taught in school. **4.** His tone is gently ironic, sarcastic, or satirical. **5.** to keep the "grand confusion of the world" under their hats, to go on with their lives as though everything were in order—and teach their children to do the same

The Vision Test

1. The speaker of the poem is waiting to take a vision test because she needs to renew her driver's license. **2.** that she is patient, slow, and nice; a kindly "priestess" with a large round, vanilla pudding, baked-apple-and-spice face; that she smiles continually **3.** "Poet." **4.** She throws back her head and laughs. **5.** Answers may vary, but could include that she mistrusts the narrator or believes her answer to this question will prove as absurd as her last answer, or that she believes that the narrator lives in a fantasy world and will give her a fantastic answer.

Page 167 Frederick Douglass and My Father's Garden

Frederick Douglass

1. Frederick Douglass **2.** air and earth **3.** It will be a part of human life, innate, unconscious, instinctive, and part of the reflexes. **4.** He means that freedom will be a natural function of the human body, as unconscious and necessary as the beating of the heart. **5.** a world where no one was ever lonely, hunted, or alien **6.** the lives that will "flesh . . . his dream," the lives of those people who will live the freedom he dreamed of

My Father's Garden

1. open hearth, white-hot, boiled, furnace, fireclay, demon, dragon, molten, blazing, satanic, cauldron **2.** a metal scrapyard

3.

Garden	Scrapyard
rockeries, grottoes, flowers petals, anthers, stalks, grapes	stoves, brake-drums, sewing machines, refrigerators, gears, cogwheels, teeth, lead, ball-bearings

4. keep his brain from melting; no, it melted anyway **5.** a "few cold scraps of Latin and Greek"; he used it to solve crossword puzzles

Page 168 Judgments and Mr. Edwards and the Spider

Judgments

1. Ellen: forty, successful, tall, well-groomed, gracious, thoughtful, a secretary; George: helps others, manages a school, never loses control; Tom: has found a role, is eminent, but doesn't have to show off his accomplishments **2.** He remembers them all gawky, afraid they weren't going to succeed, and aware of how cold and difficult the real world was. **3.** He sees that the real world really was cold and difficult and that it still is. **4.** of his "terrible poise"; and that he, like the others, "holds [the world] firmly away with gracious/gestures . . ." **5.** Answers may vary, but it seems to be that they have forgotten the truth they knew when they were younger, and in forgetting, have become less a part of the world they now hold at a distance.

Mr. Edwards and the Spider
1. spiders marching through the air from tree to tree **2.** The winds push them east to the sea, where they die. **3.** the state of sin that the Calvinists believe everyone is born into **4.** Despite their size, they hold the power to kill those more powerful than they. **5.** It is a fire so fierce and all-consuming that neither the spider nor the sinner can struggle against it; it lasts forever, and the sinner is aware of each minute of it.

Page 169 The Groundhog and Snow by Morning

The Groundhog
1. It is June in a field. **2.** At first the sight makes him dizzy or squeamish; then, with both loathing and love, he pokes at it angrily; the maggots move about more vigorously; he trembles; after controlling himself, he gets down on his knees and prays for joy. **3.** The groundhog has lost its "sap," or that which feeds life, and is only a sodden hulk. The author no longer feels the passion he felt earlier ("I lost both love and loathing") and is walled up behind his "wisdom." **4.** a bit of hair and bleached bones ("Beautiful as architecture")
5. They are all vanished, the life in great humans and great civilizations "gone" just as surely as the groundhog's vitality is gone.

Snow by Morning
1. its abundance; that it is everywhere at once
2. It spreads "like youth, like wheat" **3.** buildings become hills; sharps become round; dark, worn, noisy narrows become wide, flat, clean spaces; streets become fields; cars become fumbling sheep **4.** The first stanza speaks of a plenitude, enough for everyone "and more coming"; *manna* is food (for both mind and body) that feeds everyone, with a "loaf on every doorsill."

Page 170 Blackberry Eating and Auto Wreck

Blackberry Eating
1. eating blackberries for breakfast in late September **2.** His mood is one of pleasure: his language both describes his mood ("love") and evokes it with the sensuality of the adjectives he uses—fat, overripe, icy. **3.** They are a penalty imposed because of their knowledge of the "black art"—or magic—of making blackberries. **4.** the feel of certain "peculiar," "many-lettered, one-syllabled" words **5.** *strengths, squinched*

Auto Wreck
1. Answers may include: beating, beating; pulsing; top speed; floating down; heavy curve, dips down, brakes speed, entering; doors leap open, emptying; laid out; lifted; stowed; breaking; rocking, slightly rocking; moves out **2.** In the midst of movement and hysteria, they are "large and composed"; they sweep glass, wash away blood, make notes, and generally fix thing up, restoring the street to its previous appearance. **3.** They identify intimately with the victims; they are like convalescents recovering from their shock; they make grim jokes and "banal" resolutions; the traffic moves on slowly, but they remain, nursing this glimpse into their "richest horror." **4.** death in war, suicide, stillbirth **5.** In the poem, the auto wreck abruptly ends any chance of resolving the story, or in this case, the lives of the people in the accident are abruptly cut off from their own resolution.

Page 171 Eyes and Losses

Eyes
1. in a paddock, after dark **2.** Amanda is a horse; her eyes are like twin cigars. **3.** Her "dearest friend" is very upset about something. **4.** The sparrow is at the mercy of the hawk; the monarch butterfly is trapped in a net; a doe is being run down by dogs; her friend, in whose eyes the speaker sees a famine victim holding an empty bowl.
5. Answers may include: "burn out the dark," "take away all that is human"; comfort the speaker.

Losses
1. pilots in the armed services, soldiers, or bomber crews **2.** He means that the only reference point he and the others had for death, up until that point, was the death of a pet, an older relative, or people so far away that their deaths were meaningless. **3.** One day they were training for war; the next day they were flying in battle over England—"operational." **4.** They were all dead and their bodies all lay together. **5.** Students' portraits of the "they" in the poem will vary, but will probably refer to the men in power in any nation who make the decision to send young men off to be killed in war.

Page 172 To Be in Love and One Art

To Be in Love
1. being in love **2.** One touches things with a lighter hand, feels complete, look at things through one's lover's eyes, experiences things with one's beloved even when apart. **3.** because if she does, her pulse will tell the truth about her emotions, and she is afraid to reveal how she feels **4.** when her lover shuts the door, or is not there **5.** She means that being away from or separated from her love is a freedom she does not want. **6.** that it will turn into the "commonest ash"

One Art
1. because many things seem meant to be lost
2. One should practice losing something each day; accept the disruption that comes with loss.
3. places, names, places you meant to travel to
4. No, her tone, though light, indicates that her final loss is the hardest (harder than losing rivers and an entire continent). It is the one closest to disaster; she must make herself *write* it. **5.** "The art of losing isn't hard to master."

Page 173 Night Journey and . . . and the old women gathered

Night Journey
1. a train journey at night

2.

earth/berth	rhyme
mist/rest	slant rhyme
knees/feel	assonance
swing/ravine	consonance
blazing/bright	alliteration

3. He loves it; he says so, and stays up to watch it from his train window. **4.** rocks, suddenness, straining at a curve, muscles move with steel, swing, thunder, rush, rattles, shake, jerk, shove 5. Students' poems evoking the feeling of a journey they have made will vary.

. . . and the old women gathered
1. old women singing gospel songs 2. the old women who gather to sing (and those listening to them) 3. simile: the image is of old women standing together "like supply sergeants who have seen everything" 4. It is "fierce" and "not melodic."

Page 174 A House of Readers and Words

A House of Readers
1. reading 2. Ruth: "like a tendril growing toward the sun" Fred: "cool as a Black Angus belly-deep in a farm pond" 3. "like a farmer in the rows" 4. The mood is quiet and peaceful. The images of the tendril growing, the wedge of light, the coolness of the farm pond, the quietness of bottomland, the young corn, and the small breeze stirring the blades are all images that contribute to the mood of the poem. 5. The poet sees the children reading as elements of a natural setting, a farm, with imagery comparing Ruth to a growing tendril and Fred to a steer; the narrator himself is likened to a farmer in the field enjoying his bounty (his children); the quietness of the scene is like the bottomland where corn grows and a breeze stirs.

Words
1. words 2. a feeling of embarrassment and emptiness in them 3. They need words suitable to the way they live; familiar words, such as *linoleum, oil lamps, outhouse.* 4. because the things named are as illusive and insubstantial as ghosts to the people in the poem—and the people are haunted by them 5. *dining room, study, mantel piece, lobster thermidor, studio couch, venetian blinds, brick, fireplace* 6. the double negative, because it represents to them the most honest response to a life that is so limiting

Page 175 How I Learned English and My Father and Myself Facing the Sun

How I Learned English
1. on a baseball diamond in Williamsport, Pa. 2. a narrative or a conversational tone 3. that he has just arrived from another country and that he speaks very little English 4. The narrator, daydreaming in the outfield, gets hit in the forehead by a ball. He falls to the ground, clutching his forehead, crying out, "Oh my shin, oh my shin." 5. that he also laughed about the experience, and that Joe Barone helped him up and dusted him off 6. Student responses may vary along the lines that he is happy to be accepted and pleased with himself for "doing all right."

My Father and Myself Facing the Sun
1. the speaker and his father 2. They are both "strong, dark, bright men" dressed in western clothing, and facing the sun. 3. His father is smooth, tranquil, more accessible, represented by rounded grassy slopes; the narrator is more complex, secretive, and inaccessible, and represents himself as cracks of cliffs and gulleys. 4. They go fishing. 5. The mood of the poem is one of serenity and peacefulness, of everything being as it should be, of all the generations, father, son, grandsons, in harmony with each other and the world around them.

Page 176 The Morning My Father Died, April 7, 1963 and The Stalker

The Morning My Father Died, April 7, 1963
1. "the youngest son" of a man who has died 2. the time just before dawn 3. the cherry tree grown by the family, and a trash barrel full of smoldering trash 4. a few of the following will suffice: sight: cherry tree, smoldering trash barrel, rusty edge, colors of volcano, feathers of ash, water tank, pumice-colored hill, wheat, highway, sparrows taking flight; sound: meadowlarks, killdeer, rooster, sparrows taking off; smell: smoldering trash, sagebrush, creosote 5. trees under a lake 6. Students' answers will vary, but many will have surmised that it reflects sorrow at the loss of someone or something.

The Stalker
1. Sampt'e 2. Sampt'e shoots an arrow. 3. with wonder and wariness 4. because he put so much of himself into it that it seemed to come to life itself 5. drew . . . back, felt, wobble, go, shot, struck, glanced away, limping, settled down, approached, take flight

Page 177 Preface to a Twenty Volume Suicide Note and Prayer to the Pacific

Preface to a Twenty Volume Suicide Note
1. The ground opens up and envelops him. 2. The wind plays "broad edged silly music" 3. He's depressed, at odds with the world, possibly losing his grip on reality. 4. praying 5. Answers will vary, but he seems to be touched; it seems to give him hope.

Prayer to the Pacific
1. She is from the southwestern land "of sandrock"; she travels to the ocean. 2. the myth of origin, or creation. 3. far away, in China 4. an offering of four round stones, turquoise and coral, sent by the ocean to the speaker's people 5. how Indians arrived in this land thirty thousand years ago on the backs of giant sea turtles 6. It has been brought as a gift from the ocean ever since that time thousands of years ago. 7. It is a prayer in being a thanksgiving for the rain and an acknowledgment of the spirit of the ocean.

Page 178 Running It Backward, October Tune, and Mirror

Running it Backward
1. A movie projector is switched to reverse; the film runs backward and a man on the screen steps back from his wife's arms, which drop to her sides. He walks backward rapidly into his car just as its

door flies into his hand. Staring ahead, he reverses out of the picture. **2.** further and further into the past; he is growing younger and younger and is heading toward the time when he was not yet born **3.** a birthday party, with candles being blown out on a cake; he foresees the rapid dwindling into infancy, the loss of language, the helpless tears, and oblivion **4.** to the film that has run through the projector and is now flapping up and down

October Tune
1. a stuffed quail on the mantel, a clock chirring, a view of birch trees in the failing light **2.** He contrasts the outdoors' "hard horizon" with the quiet tranquility of the indoor scene. **3.** That person is close to the narrator of the poem, mending his clothes and keeping the corner alight with "golen hair."

Mirror
1. first person; the narrator of the story is the mirror **2.** The mirror becomes, at least metaphorically, a lake. **3.** because their soft glow obscures or hides signs of aging **4.** She hates it; seeing her aging face causes "tears and . . . agitation." She sees herself as "a terrible fish."

Page 179 History and My Father's Song

History
1. "morning sunlight lengthened in spears" establishes a mood of tranquility; the grandmother wrapped in a shawl, "eyes small with sleep," preparing chiles and *papas* establishes the comfort of the kitchen routine and introduces the poem's central figure, the grandmother **2.** First, she hoses down the walk; then, she digs up her cigar box of money and counts it twice; lastly, she buries it again somewhere else. **3.** She steals vegetables and chocolates; she is pleased with herself. **4.** She worked in the fields cutting grapes and boxing plums. **5.** He knows about her work, her medical difficulties and the tragedy of her son's death, but he doesn't know her private sorrows.

My Father's Song
1. a mood of nostalgia or melancholy **2.** his voice: the catch in in, its depth, the tremble of emotion in it **3.** flashback; the father is speaking **4.** planting corn **5.** a nest of tiny mice **6.** Students' responses may vary along these lines: He feels warmly about it. He loves the image of his grandfather's gentleness, his care of the mice, the remembered "softness," the tiny mice, and his father's voice "saying things."

Page 180 Grudnow and My Mother Pieced Quilts

Grudnow
1. the poet's grandfather **2.** because there was nothing there; it had nothing to offer **3.** a landscape without crops and trees, "scrapped raw by winter"; everything has a brown hue **4.** She would have died there. She'd have died of a childhood fever that they would not have had medicine to cure, or in one of the battles between Poland and Russia. **5.** She describes her grandfather sucking his tea through a sugar cube. **6.** The way he sipped his life in his new country, through the sweetness of his memories of life in Grudnow.

My Mother Pieced Quilts
1. She wonders how her mother put them together. **2.** to children being tucked in by their mother **3.** cotton, flannel, organdies, velvets, faded curtains, work shirt, denim, tweed, muslin, silk **4.** She is the river carrying "roaring notes" and "the caravan master at the reins" driving her "threaded needle artillery" across "mosaic cloth bridges." **5.** The quilt brings back a flood of memories, which cause her to both laugh and cry.

Page 181 Easter

1. turtles **2.** They moved around constantly, like rabbits. **3.** "Shhh. Be quiet. Lie still." **4.** how explosive they are **5.** why they don't fall **6.** parents rushing to save them **7.** Grandma Tollefson has turned off her hearing aid and can't hear her grandson well at all. Perhaps this is why her grandson's playing reminds her of the guitarist she loved so long ago. **8.** They are looking at the Buehlers' wedding album and laughing. **9.** It is like an ocean wave about to break. **10.** fishing at five in the morning in the cold of Lake Wobegon, smelling the lake and his uncle's coffee when he was nine years old **11.** Answers will vary, but should be humorous.

Page 182 from The Lonely Hunter

1. afraid, a little homesick, but observing everything **2.** because Claire convinced Carson to keep their money together; shortly thereafter, the purse was lost or stolen, leaving both penniless **3.** She is afraid, lonely; fascinated but repelled by the noise and dirt, the poverty and the wealth. **4.** during the decade of the Great Depression; the 1930s **5.** She worked as a typist, a ledger clerk and receptionist, a waitress, an editor, and a dog walker. She was fired from at all of her jobs; the only one she was any good at was walking dogs. **6.** She hears someone playing "wonderful Mozart" and knocks on the door to find out who is playing; she becomes friends with the pianist. **7.** sights: loads of cargo being slung aboard ship, dollies and forklifts in constant motion, longshoremen, wharf rats pilfering cargo, pigeons feeding on sacks of grain, fog drifting in, crew wandering back late; sounds: longshoremen shouting, chattering, and whistling signals, the electric motors whining, the winches squealing, pigeons cooing, fog signals, whistles and bells of distant ships, the crew whispering, singing ribald songs **8.** She yearns to be part of it all; she wants to travel, and dreams of the faraway and the unattainable. **9.** Students' responses may vary along the lines that she is more confident, more aggressive, better able to take care of herself, less susceptible to homesickness, etc.

Page 183 from Blue Highways

1. because he has a lot of memories of the roads that he associates with his estranged wife, called

Cherokee **2.** He is going to stay off the major interstates and instead follow the small backroads, which are called "blue highways" because they used to be shown in blue on maps to distinguish them from the red of the main routes. **3.** Ghost Dancing **4.** The author watches a man who is straightening a doorway in a old two-story house that has a log cabin buried under the siding. The two men talk about log cabins and the history of the building that's being worked on. He ends up envying the fact that the builder is using the past to build something new. **5.** near a spring under sycamore trees, as he has lunch **6.** He counts the number of calendars in a café; the more calendars, the better the food. **7.** Answers may vary. He seems to be disillusioned and cynical; he seeks harmony, makes people think he needs cheering up, and doesn't mind being scared; he wants to meet people. **8.** When the Post Office told the citizens they had to choose a name, they got together and searched for a name. By the end of the evening, they had not agreed on a name, but they did agree that "this here's a nameless place. . . ." The name stuck. **9.** They are very friendly and open their doors to him, feeding him and sharing their lives with him. **10.** Answers will vary, but should note that he seems to have mellowed.

Page 184 from Hunger of Memory

1. Reading is something they do "out of necessity and as quickly as possible"; their reading is practical and utilitarian: work manuals, prayer books, newspapers, and recipes. **2.** He wondered what the relationship between learning and reading was; he felt isolated and lonely when he read; reading was a chore and he didn't see how books could be his best friend. **3.** He realizes that books were going to make him "educated," and that result was one he trusted. **4.** His teachers praise him for reading; at home, his mother wonders what he "sees" in his books, whether or not so much reading is healthy, and whether or not the author is simply trying to get out of working. **5.** He uses language of the senses to describe his pleasure in reading: "mysterious comfort . . . reading in the dawn quiet," the "blue-gray silence interrupted by the . . . churning of the refrigerator motor . . ." or warm, summer evenings, when he read in twilight to the "cool, whirring sounds of the sprinklers." **6.** He liked the warmth and charm of *The Human Comedy*, by William Saroyan, but doubted it could be "important" because it was so pleasurable. He liked the fictional world in which he was immersed when reading Dickens, but he didn't like the way the story ended, with everything neatly resolved. **7.** He means that he read in too directed a way, searching only for one thing that would "fill the hollow within": education. He did not have his own point of view when he read, which would have allowed him to understand what he read in a different way. **8.** Answers will vary.

Page 185 from To Be Young, Gifted and Black

1. the impulse to tell the story of one's life **2.** Her parents gave their children little in the way of caresses but everything they needed to survive; the children were taught to be proud of their heritage, to struggle, and to succeed at what they did; they were passionate in what they thought and felt, but were embarrassed by open shows of affection. **3.** She remembers the street rhymes and games and wonders what their meaning for her life might be ("A giant step to *where*?"); she remembers the hot summer nights her family slept in the park to stay cool, and her father telling her about the stars, and her inability to comprehend their distance from her. **4.** Students will use their own words to describe the author's father, who is physically and intellectually commanding, a man kings would have imitated; a man always doing something brilliant, studying law, inventing things, talking about history and private enterprise; seemingly fearless. **5.** The letter is addressed to the Editor of The *New York Times* and was written by the author, Lorraine Hasberry. **6.** the "restrictive covenants" that prevented blacks from living where they wanted to in Chicago **7.** She had to live in a hostile, white neighborhood where "howling mobs" surrounded her family's house, threatening the author and her family's lives; she had to endure being spat at, cursed, and hit every day in order to get to school. Her mother patrolled the house at night with a gun, while her father fought the battle in court. **8.** Even though he won the Supreme Court decision, blacks in Chicago remained restricted to the ghettos they fought to get out of, and he died a bitter exile. **9.** American way, white neighborhood, correct way of fighting, respectable part of the battle, won, progress, bitterness; students' responses to second half of question—whether the author's ironic tone is a good choice—will vary, but most will agree it is forceful and effective.

Page 186 from Shadow and Act

1. Learn to wear it and make it our own, charge it with our emotions, make it a mask and a shield. **2.** Blacks bear the names of their ancestor's slave owners and are reminded constantly of that heritage. **3.** that they represent a "triumph of the spirit" over the horrors of slavery; they represent transformation and the will to survive **4.** He says that in their own communities, these same children exhibit a great facility with language; he says that language skills "depend . . . upon a knowledge of the details . . . of a given environment"—a very different environment from the schools that teach reading. **5.** He was always puzzled by it, not understanding what a poet was nor why his father named him after one. **6.** the poet Ralph Waldo Emerson **7.** because he loved to read and because he admired the works of Ralph Waldo Emerson, "poet and philosopher" **8.** The boy next door was named Emerson, which confused the author because he thought he was being mistaken for him. **9.** He compares his name to a wonderful lens he found that he played with, but which he had no idea how to use correctly. He could not make the lens "yield its secret" nor could he discard it—just as with his name. **10.** Students should describe a friend's—or their own—nickname and why that name is appropriate or inappropriate.

Page 187 Nobel Acceptance Speech
1. in that he accepts the honor on behalf of all of the people who perished in the Holocaust as well as those who survived. **2.** Elie Wiesel, the author **3.** It means evil, and specifically, the evil of those who tortured and murdered six million European jews; the young boy discovered evil when he discovered this kingdom. **4.** Then he asked if what was happening could really be taking place in the twentieth century; now he asks what the author has done with his life. **5.** He says that he is trying to keep the memory of the Holocaust alive, to keep people from forgetting. He says that they were naive, that the world *did* know about the Holocaust and still remained silent. He believes people must interfere. **6.** He swears never to be silent "whenever and wherever human beings endure suffering and humiliation," because silence always helps the oppressors and not the victims. **7.** when human lives are in danger; when human dignity is jeopardized; when people are persecuted because of race, religion, or political views **8.** the fight against apartheid, the plight of the Palestinians, the denial of Lech Walesa's right to dissent in Poland, the violation of human rights everywhere (or similar answers) **9.** that they are not alone, that someone is speaking out on their behalf **10.** people in desperate need of our help **11.** Students answers will vary.

Page 188 The Man in the Water
1. the bridge (full of traffic), the location of the event in Washington, D.C., and the contrast between the blue and green of the Air Florida jet and the the icy chunks in the river **2.** He says that the nation might have seen something "successful about their makeup" in this event: human nature rising to the occasion. **3.** the person known as "the man in the water" **4.** Whenever a lifeline and flotation ring was lowered to him, he passed it on to another passenger; by the time the helicopter came back for him, he had gone under. **5.** It gives him universality; they see his heroic actions as proof "that no man is ordinary." **6.** The fact that he, like everyone else on the plane, must have wanted terribly to live, and must have known that he would not live if he kept on handing the rope and ring to the others. **7.** the battle between humans and nature **8.** Even though he died, he, by his actions, had the power to hand life over "to a stranger," which is, the author concludes, a power of nature and as such a part of it. **9.** Students' responses will vary in explaining which of the people they think they would most resemble.

Unit 8 The Red Badge of Courage

Page 189 The Red Badge of Courage: Chapters 1 and 2
1. They are Union, or Federal, soldiers fighting for the North. **2.** The tall soldier says that the army is due to fight the next day. The loud soldier disagrees, stating that the army is "set" and has been ready to move eight times so far and hasn't yet moved. **3.** He returns to his tent to be alone with his thoughts. **4.** He feels that men now are "better, or more timid." Education has taught men to be civilized, or financial matters have dampened their passions. **5.** The flashback tells of the youth's desire to enlist, his enlistment in the army, his mother's reaction to it, her farewell to her son, the youth's early days in the army and the soldiers' reception in the towns they passed through, and his arrival at his current state of mind as a result of having been camped in the same place for so long. **6.** He wonders whether or not he will run away once he is engaged in battle. **7.** He is relieved to discover that everyone isn't as confident of their response to actual fighting as they seem to be. Like him, they are untried and unsure. **8.** The rumor turns out to be false; the army does not march the next day. **9.** that they are all heroes, and that they are all as terrified as he is. **10.** like two snakes crawling from a dark cavern **11.** The youth accuses the loud soldier of thinking that he is the bravest man in the world, which angers the loud soldier, who only claims that he will try to fight the best he can. The youth grows angry because he can't find his own doubts reflected in anyone else. **12.** Answers will vary, but should include those passages that show Henry is afraid that he might be the only one who will run when confronted with battle, that he can find no one with whom to talk about his fears, that show the youth feels alone while everyone about him laughs and discusses the military plan, that when they break for the night, the youth sits away from the others and feels isolated and unhappy.

Page 190 The Red Badge of Courage: Chapters 3 and 4
1. The men shed their knapsacks and heavy clothing and travel light. However, they still travel in large groups, unlike veterans who work in small groups, they are all wearing new hats, and the flag is still colorful, its pole polished. **2.** "One gray dawn, however, he was kicked in the leg by the tall soldier . . ." **3.** He feels like a helpless child, carried along by the mob; he thinks about escape but sees that he is trapped by the regiment and by the "iron laws of tradition" as if in a moving box. He thinks he is going to be killed. **4.** knots of skirmishers running here and there; "little combats" **5.** ominous and threatening; he suddenly feels that they are all being marched into a trap **6.** He becomes impatient and distraught; the strain of waiting and worrying about the battle unnerves him. **7.** He hands the youth a packet of mementos that he wants the youth to take to his family because he is certain that he is going to die in this first encounter. **8.** Some of the rumors indicate that the youth's side in the war is being trounced by the rebels; other rumors indicate that the rebels are being soundly beaten. **9.** The officer's swearing sounds so ordinary, it's as if he accidently hit his fingers with a hammer. **10.** He resolves to get a good look at the "monster" that has caused the troops to flee, and thinks once he has seen it, he will run "better than the best of them." **11.** At first, the battle is at a distance. The fighting regiments are nearby, however. Then he can hear the

whistling of the bullets and see men getting wounded and dying. Finally, the troops in front of him begin to flee and he and the others watch them as they whirl past in a panic.

Page 191 The Red Badge of Courage: Chapters 5 and 6

1. to waiting in a village street before the arrival of the circus parade **2.** as if seven hundred bonnets were being tried on: the adjusting of the cartridge boxes prior to battle; like a wet parrot: the way in which the colonel scolds the men; like that of a weeping urchin: the way Henry's face is sweating and soiled; like a firework: the way the regiment begins to fire its volleys **3.** Answers may include that he stops thinking about himself and becomes a part of the whole; he becomes "welded into a common personality," and becomes aware of his comrades; he feels the potency of the "battle brotherhood," the "mysterious fraternity" of the group. **4.** Some begin to shout and cheer, others are silent. Henry feels joy that he now has time to look around him. **5.** the calm persistence of Nature in the middle of all the fighting **6.** They believe the battle is over, but the enemy is renewing the assault on the regiment. **7.** They groan and become sullen, complaining to one another that they didn't come to "fight the hull rebel army." **8.** The youth waits for the "red and green monster" to devour him; near him a man stops and runs, howling, and another man throws down his rifle and flees. Soon others begin to run, and the youth snaps out of his trance, turns, and runs also. **9.** He feels amazement and pity for the men still fighting, who he thinks are fools for not realizing the peril they are in; he wants to thrash the general, who, he feels, is criminal in not attempting to save the situation. **10.** At the start of the chapter, he is proud and self-satisfied that he has stayed with the regiment and fought valiantly. At the end of the chapter, he is terrified, running frantically from the war monster.

Page 192 The Red Badge of Courage: Chapters 7, 8, and 9

1. He learns that his side has won the battle after all. He is amazed and angry; he feels "wronged" because he fled to save himself from annihilation while "fools" stayed on facing death. Finally he begins to feel pity for himself. **2.** He heaves a pine cone at a squirrel, which runs in fear; the youth concludes that it is a law of Nature to run from danger. **3.** the sight of a dead man proped against a tree, his face being grazed by ants **4.** He wants to see what is happening for the same reason that anyone who had a chance to see "the earth and moon" collide would rush to see such a spectacular event. **5.** He realizes that the battle he fought in was a "perfunctory popping"—a very small battle in comparison to what is going on now. **6.** It is an "immense and terrible machine," grinding up and spitting out men. **7.** The tattered man begins talking to the youth about the greatness of the fight they have just been in (assuming the youth to have been fighting with him). The tattered man then asks the youth where he has been hit, and the youth suddenly turns away, leaving the tattered man staring after him. **8.** He is ashamed that he doesn't have a wound as the other soldiers do. **9.** It refers to a wound, gotten in battle, that proves the courage of the person who has been wounded. **10.** He is Jim Conklin, the tall soldier, who first brought news that the regiment would soon be engaged in battle and who told Henry that he'd run if the others ran and fight if the others fought. **11.** that he won't be able to get out of the way of the artillery wagons and will be run over by them **12.** In Chapter 7, the youth sees a man who has been long dead and who is gradually being absorbed into Nature: this sight fills him with horror and fear. In Chapter 9, the youth watches his friend and comrade Jim Conklin as he is dying: to the youth this sight is both compelling and enraging. At this point, rage replaces fear and shame, and his deep identification with Conklin gives Henry the courage to seek the battlefield once again.

Page 193 The Red Badge of Courage: Chapters 10 and 11

1. He is amazed at Conklin's strength, the way he jigged and danced before he died; he says he's never seen anything like it before. **2.** The tattered man is not feeling well, and the youth fears that he may have to witness yet another death. **3.** He is the soldier who told the tattered man that he had been wounded; at the end of the chapter, the tattered man mistakes the youth for Tom Jamison. **4.** The tattered man asks the youth where his wound is located. **5.** because he can't bear to have questions asked about a wound he doesn't have; he doesn't want to admit the truth about his actions in battle. **6.** He wishes he were dead; he feels even worse about himself after leaving the tattered man, perhaps to die, wandering confusedly in the field. **7.** The mood is one of fear and haste, alive with the deafening sounds of battle. **8.** He starts to feel better, thinking that perhaps he isn't so bad after all for having fled himself. **9.** seeing the column of replacements rushing into the heart of the battle; he believes they are heroes and, in comparison, his deeds seem even worse than they had before. **10.** He thinks about picking up a gun and returning to fight. **11.** If his side wins it will be a "roundabout vindication" of his own cowardice, but if they lose, his running will seem as though it were prophetic of the outcome of the battle. **12.** Responses will vary along the lines that Henry Fleming is a very young man floundering in a terrifying situation. He wants to be brave and do what is expected of him, but he panics, along with many others. Because of his actions, he discovers a "capacity for self-hate" in himself, he sees himself as a "craven loon," and he tries desperately to rationalize his behavior. He fears the disdain of his comrades even as he loathes himself.

Page 194 The Red Badge of Courage, Chapters 12 and 13

1. They come charging out of the woods like "terrified buffaloes." **2.** He calls war the "red animal" and the "blood-swollen god." **3.** The man hits Henry on the head with his rifle. **4.** He thinks about his mother's cooking—the special meals she made for him—and of the table and walls in the kitchen. He remembers swimming in the pool—the clothes left in disarray and the water on his body. **5.** He doesn't seem upset at the confusion and terror of the day's fighting, and talks about how he thought he was from everywhere from Ohio to Florida; he teases about an officer possibly losing a leg; chats about the death of his friend John, and then wonders again how they will find their regiments. **6.** When he meets the tattered man, the youth has not been wounded in battle and the questions the tattered man asks make the youth feel ashamed of himself; when the tattered man needs assistance, the youth leaves. When he meets the cheery man, the youth has been "wounded," so he no longer feels wary of being questioned; he himself needs assistance at this point and allows himself to be guided by the cheery man. **7.** He tells the sentry that he has seen terrible fighting and that he has been separated from the regiment and shot in the head. **8.** The corporal tells the youth that his wound is a "queer lump almost as if some feller had lammed yeh on th' head with a club," which is just the way the youth did get his wound. **9.** He sees his comrades in various poses of battle exhaustion, the red glow of the fire reflected on them. The mood created is eerie, "lit with a phosphorescent glow," making it seem as if the soldiers had just had a wild time at their "feast of war," and are now exhausted from the effort. **10.** The loud soldier, Wilson, comes and gives Henry coffee, washes and wraps Henry's "wound," and puts Henry to bed wrapped up in his own blankets. **11.** Students' letters will vary as they describe the wounded Henry from Wilson's sympathetic point of view.

Page 195 The Red Badge of Courage: Chapters 14, 15, and 16

1. that he has wakened in a charnel place—a place where the dead are brought **2.** Wilson does not seem to be worrying about his personal prowess or his accomplishments, he doesn't get upset at imagined digs at his abilities. He shows a quiet and humble assurance that he hasn't had before. **3.** Wilson tries to break up a fight between two men, where previously he might have fought himself. **4.** Answers will vary. He might be insinuating that Henry ran when he observes that half the regiment had scattered all over, wandering around like Henry. **5.** He sees it as a weapon with which to defend himself from his friend's possibly probing questions. **6.** He feels unconcerned; he has learned from his experiences that even if he is a coward, chance may still protect him; furthermore, he has had experience of war and feels that it is not as frightening as it has been made out. **7.** Answers may include: He feels superior because he hasn't been caught in his lies; he feels superior to his friend, who has to admit his weakness; he feels himself to be generous for having refrained from making a comment on his friend's foolishness; he feels strong and stout, as if he is "an individual of extraordinary virtues"; he feels that others will admire him. **8.** The mood is one of despair at the rumors that the army is being beaten again. **9.** He is afraid that the sarcastic man might know something about his cowardice of the previous day; he shuts up and becomes "a modest person." **10.** He hears Henry cursing at the people in charge for running them around "like rats." **11.** He goes from being proud and boastful about his experience as a soldier, to being afraid that his cowardice will be exposed by the sarcastic man, to being irritated at the way the battle is being fought.

Page 196 The Red Badge of Courage, Chapters 17, 18, and 19

1. He is with the rest of his regiment in the woods awaiting the chance to fight in the raging battle. **2.** He is filled with hatred and rage toward the enemy. **3.** The youth is so caught up in the battle that he fires even when there is nothing to fire on. The others are impressed with his fierceness in battle. **4.** Answers may vary, but it would seem that Henry's reactions have been purely instinctive, reflexive. His so-called heroism was accomplished in a state much like sleep. **5.** They go in search of a stream where they can find water for themselves and others of the regiment. **6.** They learn that the enemy's next charge may break their line, and that the 304th regiment—their own regiment—is to move in to fill in the gap. They overhear a general and another officer talking. **7.** They know that the general has referred to their regiment in insulting words as being mule drivers rather than fighters, and they also know that the general doesn't believe that many of the regiment will return from the charge of the enemy's lines. **8.** a barrage of intense shooting **9.** The men are being led in a charge against intense enemy opposition; they have paused briefly, stunned by the intensity of fire that they are receiving. They have been swept up by a powerful and deadly force beyond their control and beyond their comprehension. **10.** the Union flag **11.** In this battle, he rushes forward despite the danger, leading the men in the regiment; he doesn't run or suffer from doubts as in the first battle.

Page 197 The Red Badge of Courage: Chapters 20, 21, and 22

1. He becomes the color-bearer, now that the soldier previously carrying the colors has been shot. **2.** They are in disarray; having made their initial assault on the enemy, they are stunned by the force of the battle and have fallen back to a clump of trees. **3.** The men think they'll surely be beaten this time, but they beat back an enemy attack; the "small duel" between the two forces proves that the regiment can win against their enemy. **4.** He can't believe that the distance of the clump of trees is so near, nor that the span of time that the regiment was fighting was so brief. **5.** He says the colonel's regiment made a mess of the battle and that his soldiers are a bunch of mud diggers. He tells the colonel that they could have had great success if they had only gone a hundred more feet. **6.** They are bewildered and angry at the general's lack of appreciation for their extreme efforts in the battle, but they begin to believe what he has said about them. **7.** They are told that the general said they both deserve to be made major generals. **8.** He is serene, full of confidence, and unafraid. **9.** four **10.** He remembers the general calling the regiment "mule drivers" and "mud diggers," and he resolves to fight to the end and yield no ground. **11.** They are very weak, and their numbers are few. Many are wounded and bleeding. They seem drained of spirit and energy.

Page 198 The Red Badge of Courage, Chapters 23 and 24

1. He is surprised that, though very weary, they quickly respond and surge forward with new force to meet the challenge. **2.** He captures the enemy's flag. **3.** the capture of the enemy flag and of four enemy soldiers **4.** Students' responses may vary along the lines that he is proud of himself, tired, and ready to congratulate himself and his friend for their part in the battle. **5.** It describes the end of the battle in which the regiment had been fighting. **6.** He has to adjust his senses to the new circumstances; his brain has to throw off its "battleful ways" and begin to think again about matters outside of fighting. He has to start thinking about himself again. **7.** At first he feels shame and embarrassment when he thinks about his flight from his first battle. Then he begins to rationalize, thinking that fleeing was a natural mistake of a "novice." Finally, he realizes that he was foolish in trying to escape the battle. **8.** the memory of the tattered solider; because he realizes that the tattered man's concerns were for the youth's injuries rather than for his own, even though he was near death; Henry is ashamed that he abandoned the man rather than helping him **9.** He comes to believe that he can use his mistake as a learning experience, something that will deflate his ego and help him to be a gentle, caring man. **10.** Students' responses as to whether Henry has changed may vary, but most will agree that, having seen battle, he has a new perspective on his place in the universe—as a small part of it and not as its center; that he has acquired a calm assurance of his abilities; a knowledge of himself that he has acquired from acting less well than he had expected and then doing better; that he has acquired humility about himself from examining his shortcomings; etc.

Unit 8 Three Long Stories

Page 199 Four Meetings

1. He is visiting the New England home of a friend named Latouche at Christmas. A party is being given in their honor. At this party, the narrator is introduced to Miss Caroline Spencer, to whom he shows photographs of Europe. **2.** She is charming, pretty, very small, almost thirty; she is shy and soft-spoken, "artistic," and very pleased to be looking at the narrator's pictures of Europe. **3.** She has been saving her money in order to travel to Europe. **4.** in that she thinks about Europe all the time, which prevents her from dealing with things at home **5.** the passion for the picturesque **6.** thinking about traveling to Europe all of the time **7.** The narrator, who has been living in Paris for three years, goes to Havre to meet his sister and her husband. There he discovers that his sister is ill and in bed. He and his brother-in-law walk around Havre, where, at a cafe, the narrator sees the familiar face of Caroline Spencer. **8.** They traveled to Europe on the same steamer. **9.** She is very excited and happy to be in Europe. **10.** He has gone to the bank to change her money into French coins. **11.** Her cousin has something "particular" to say to her, and she seems to be worried about what it is. **12.** He thinks her cousin is a "queer fellow" with "treacherous" eyes, and he wonders what he is "up to." **13.** She is "completely changed." She has been crying and is very sad. **14.** He tells her that he needs money because he is in debt; he wants her to give him her travel money, which he will pay back when his "great picture" has been finished. She agrees to do so. **15.** The Countess ran away to marry Caroline's cousin, for which act she was disinherited by her father. Caroline thinks the story is very sad and romantic. Because of it, she is willing to sacrifice her hard-earned savings. **16.** He is angry that she believes her cousin's tale and has given her money to him. **17.** His friend Latouche has died, and he is making a condolence call to his mother. **18.** She seems to think very little of her; she is quite sarcastic in gesture and word about the Countess. **19.** She seems much older, and looks tired and wasted. **20.** He reminds her of her anticipation about traveling in Europe and the way in which her trip ended. **21.** The Countess arrived on Caroline Spencer's doorstep after her husband died. She has been living with Caroline two years. Caroline Spencer waits on the Countess because that is what the Countess expects. **22.** Caroline Spencer's only current or future experience of "dear old Europe" is in her unhappy encounters with the disagreeable, fraudulent French Countess, who represents Europe's most un-picturesque aspects. **23.** Students' responses to the question of whether or not they feel sympathy for Caroline Spencer will vary.

Page 201 Afterward

1. flashback **2.** England **3.** The Boynes are a married American couple who have come to England to find a romantically uncomfortable country place, preferably with a ghost, to live in. **4.** It doesn't reveal itself immediately; in fact, it isn't until long afterward that people even realize there has been a ghost. **5.** The Blue Star Mine has given the Boynes a windfall **6.** They like its sense of the past, its quietness and solitude, and its remoteness. **7.** He seems anxious, worried, and withdrawn; she feels he is hiding something. **8.** only that there is supposed to be one **9.** She and Ned found a hidden stairway leading to a ledge overlooking the downs; from this vantage point, they saw a shadowy figure walking by their house. Ned dashed down the stairs to find the mysterious visitor, but the visitor had disappeared. **10.** He claims that he thought the man was Peters, their stable man, and that he wanted to ask Peters a question. **11.** Mary doesn't realize that there has been a ghost until some time after the ghost has appeared. (Ned, too, seems to have had a delayed reaction.) **12.** It contains a newspaper clipping that tells about a lawsuit filed against Ned by someone involved with Ned in the Blue Star Mine. **13.** She feels guilty because she knows so little about Ned's business; she is afraid that she has been "too easily put off" by his assurances from inquiring very deeply into them. **14.** because the suit had no chance for success **15.** Students' opinions of Ned's explanation will vary; some may believe he is hiding something; others may feel it is settled business. **16.** The house wraps her up in a sense of security—it is "in the air," and flashes "out at her from the fire." The house creates in her a sense of well-being. **17.** He is young and slight and has a faintly American accent. He wears a soft felt hat, which throws a shadow on his face. He seems weary and dejected when he is told he can't see Boyne. **18.** Her husband has gone out with a visitor and hasn't returned. **19.** the pale young stranger she had met in the garden **20.** that she and Ned used to call England "a confoundedly hard place to get lost in," and now Ned himself is lost and cannot be found. **21.** the identity of Parvis, a Waukesha lawyer and "possible intermediary" in the Elwell case. (He has no information about Ned, however.) **22.** No, she is sure he will never return. **23.** She discovers that her husband took advantage of Elwell to make money in the Blue Star Mine, and that Elwell shot himself as a result, taking nearly two months to die. **24.** He is the man she saw in the garden—the man who left with her husband. **25.** Dialogues written by students will vary.

Page 203 Tom Outland's Story

1. a string of events, starting with a poker game **2.** Answers will vary, but may include: Six or seven men are playing a high-stakes poker game, while many others watch. One man, a dirty, unkempt fellow named Rodney Blake, is in the process of winning a succession of jackpots, which makes the other men in the game angry. **3.** Students' responses will vary along the lines that each is generous and honest, and willing to look after the interests of others. **4.** Tom has been sick with pneumonia and both his doctor and priest tell him he must give up his night job and work in the open in order to regain his health. **5.** He does Tom's share of the work, even though Tom is healthy enough to do it himself, and he makes sure that Tom reads one hundred lines of Latin every day. **6.** Section II opens at a cabin in New Mexico; it is outdoors, away from civilization, isolated, and clean and pure. In contrast, the adobe room that opened Section I was a dirty, crowded place in town, full of men gambling and indulging other vices. **7.** trying to climb the mesa **8.** Answers may vary, but should indicate that they love watching the way light and weather play over it; they are tantalized by it and want to explore it; it puts their camp in shadow early in the afternoon when the sun sets, and it dominates their camp. **9.** He finds an ancient irrigation main and Indian artifacts: arrowheads, broken pottery, and a stone pickax. **10.** He likes it better than any other place he's ever been, and feels delight in it every time he walks out the door of the cabin. **11.** Henry Atkins, an old Englishman found living on handouts in Tarpin. **12.** He's clean and tidy and keeps the cabin very homelike; he's "polite and mannerly," as simple and kind as a child; he holds no grudges against any of the people who have taken advantage of him. **13.** an ancient city of stone, tucked a thousand feet up into the face of a cliff **14.** He is awestruck by the beauty and symmetry of what he sees. He understands how rare and wonderful it is, and has trouble describing it. **15.** They plan to find a trail down the north end of the mesa and spend the summer exploring it. **16.** They find a trail leading from the box canyon, cutting down trees to bridge the gaps in the steep path. **17.** They begin excavating the ruins, collecting and numbering the specimens, and logging them in Tom's day book. **18.** that they did everything with "patience and deliberation" and must have been a fine people. **19.** the name given to the body of a woman found by Tom and Blake in the ruins (she seemed to have been murdered when she was young) **20.** While trying to reach some ruins, Henry stands on Tom's shoulders to reach the cavern. A snake strikes him in the forehead, and he dies two hours later. **21.** He guesses that the tribe was wiped out while in their summer camp along the river by a nomadic tribe that wanted their hides, clothing, and weapons. **22.** Tom hopes to be able to convince an expect to come out to study the remains; Blake seems to hope for a reward of some kind. **23.** Because his business is with living Indians, he tells Tom, not dead ones. **24.** If he wants to get their attention, he must take them to lunch. **25.** He is depressed by the pettiness of their lives, their scheming to get ahead on what little they make, and by their need to appear to be better off than they are. It seems to him that they and others like them are living a form of slavery. **26.** Blake has sold artifacts they'd found to a German, Fechtig, for a lot of money. **27.** because in Tom's eyes he has sold out his country by selling the artifacts—he is a traitor **28.** Students' interpretations of Blake's meaning will vary, but he may mean that he'd be ashamed to have treated Tom the way Tom has treated him. He could also mean that he'd hate to see his friend hurt the way he has been. **29.** because he is sorry for the way he has treated Blake **30.** studying Spanish and Latin and cleaning up the mess left on the mesa, he is supremely happy, full of rare energy; he feels as if he has "found everything, instead of having lost everything" **31.** probably that he realizes he valued his feelings about the artifacts more than his friendship with Blake; that he'd lost sight of the fact that what Blake did—though wrong, perhaps—was done because he loved Tom and wanted the best for him